# The Wolf in Winter

# The Wolf in Winter

## A Story of Francis of Assisi

### John Sacke

Paulist Press
New York/Mahwah

*To the nearest miss—*
*my daughter Bryana—*
*and her big brother Bjorn*

Cover and interior illustrations by Gloria Ortiz

Library of Congress
Catalog Card Number: 85-60296

ISBN: 0-8091-6556-2

Published by Paulist Press
997 Macarthur Boulevard
Mahwah, New Jersey 07430

Printed and bound in the
United States of America

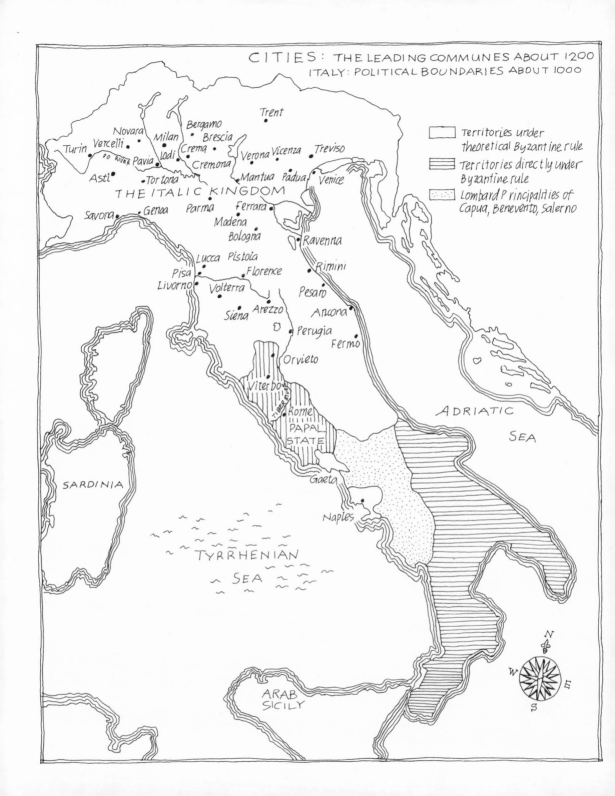

CITIES: THE LEADING COMMUNES ABOUT 1200
ITALY: POLITICAL BOUNDARIES ABOUT 1000

Territories under
theoretical Byzantine rule

Territories directly under
Byzantine rule

Lombard Principalities of
Capua, Benevento, Salerno

Trent

Novara  Bergamo
Vercelli  Milan  Brescia
Turin  Lodi  Crema
PO RIVER  Pavia  Verona Vicenza  Treviso
Asti  Cremona
Tortona  Mantua  Padua  Venice
THE ITALIC KINGDOM

Savona  Genoa  Parma  Ferrara
Modena  Ravenna
Bologna
Rimini
Lucca  Pistoia
Pisa  Florence  Pesaro
Livorno  Volterra  Ancona
Siena  Arezzo  Perugia  Fermo
Orvieto

Viterbo
ADRIATIC
TIBER RIVER
Rome
SEA
PAPAL
STATE

Gaeta

SARDINIA
Naples

TYRRHENIAN

SEA

N
W    E
S

ARAB
SICILY

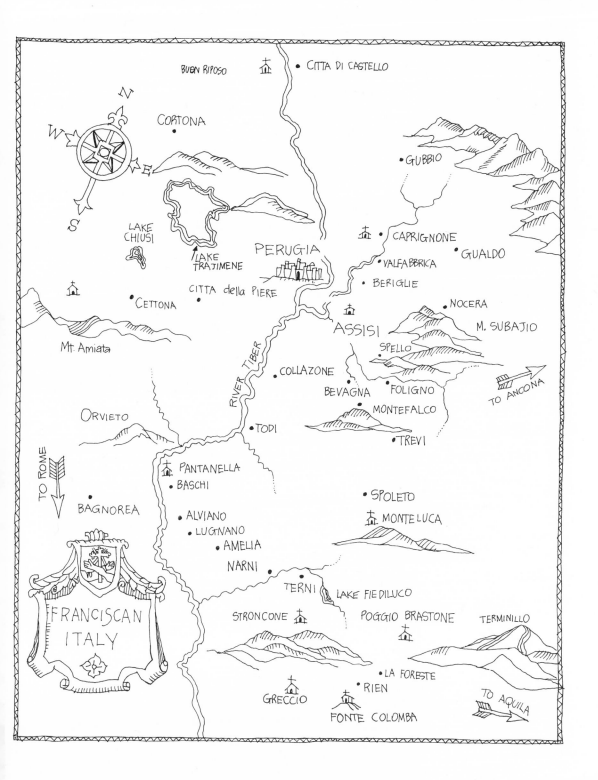

# Prologue

"Following the example of the ancient priest who is said to have travelled thousands of miles caring naught for his provisions and attaining the state of sheer ecstasy under the pure beams of the moon, I left my broken house on the River Sumida."

Basho, *The Records of a Weather-Exposed Skeleton*, 1685

Basho's description of Komon (Kuang-wên), a Chinese priest of the Nansung dynasty (1127–1279), could be applied equally to the wanderings of Francis of Assisi during the same period. This story tries to recapture the first few steps and the setting of that journey.

1

# 1

## Lupo

Gubbio grips the slope of Mount Ingino with all the tenacity and seriousness of a medieval fortress, stern as the cliffs rising behind it. It was the same in March of 1207. The city towers and battlements on its outer walls had purpose then, protecting it from the raiders who poured out of Perugia, ruinous as the snow-swollen rivers raging down the sides of Ingino.

On top of the mountain, the monastery of San Ubaldo guarded the city and the Apennine passes. Even the blue-green cypresses ranged in columns on the hills had the appearance of sentinels. With the stiff movement of chilled watchdogs, their shadows stretched through the lavender dawn, patrolling patches of mud and dirty snow, leaping the low stone walls and grape stalks of the smallholdings outside the city.

3

"Another night passed safely," they whispered as they brushed Gubbio's eastern gate, the Porta di San Agostino, still barred shut against the world. The mountain top responded with the morning song of the monks:

Lord, Omnipotent God,
Who have brought us
To the start of this new day,
Keep us in Your power
That no evil threaten us ...

Though the cypresses had succumbed by midday to the sudden steamy heat and curled their drugged shades around their trunks, by evening out the shadows raced again, full-stride across the leprosarium and the fig and olive groves at its foot, across the next ridge where the sheep were bedding down, to the ridge beyond, to the very edge of the oak forest that curved like the keen edge of a butcher's blade around the sheepfold. The wind hurled the javelin chants of the monks into the dark heart of this danger, now a prayer of urgent warning:

Brothers, be sober and watchful,
For the devil, your adversary,
Makes his rounds like a roaring lion,
Seeking whom he can devour...
Lord, have mercy on us...

For another shadow danced within the forest—a gray ghost playing in and out beneath the arching Holm Oaks, tangled lattices that held out snow and sun alike. Too soon to be about, he knew, still too much twilight, too close to man and his dogs, but the hunger that had driven him for days had overwhelmed his caution, made him too impatient to wait for the deep night when his predations could be carried out unseen.

He loped smoothly, in spite of the aching in his fore-legs, his shoulders rising and falling to the spring hymn surging once more

4

through him—though spring held little promise for him now. His only mate had been killed years before by the men. His sons and daughters hunted through the wilder northern woods for deer and rabbits, mountain sheep and grouse—as he would if he had the speed. At sixteen years he slowed the pack, no longer had the strength nor skill to face a cornered boar. But sheep, weak ewes and lambs, he could still chase down and drag into his woods.

He trotted to the crossing of two paths, then stopped to sniff a wheel rim propped on its broken axle. For years the wheel had been a message post for the forest animals. He sniffed for signs of his own kind, knowing he would find none. He was the last in the wilderness above the city. And worse, the scents he found were mingled strongly with the smell of dogs.

He hated dogs! He remembered well the pack that had cornered his mate until the hunters came with their spears and brutal clubs. None of the dogs had dared to challenge her alone.

He sprayed the wheel and moved on, running again as he broke through the thin snow crust of an open meadow, the last snow of the season. A part of him could still exult in spring, which meant more and easier prey, warmer nights, and some resurgence of his faded powers. Life would be easier now until the snows returned.

He slowed to a trot as he neared the edge of the forest. Ahead was the hillside where the grasses thrust their tufts through shale and gravel and snow, surviving the onslaughts of weather and terrain and the sheep who grazed them back to roots time and again. Ahead were the sheep themselves, huddling together in the woolly mist.

He caught the smell of nearby carrion. He sniffed until he found it, a chunk of mutton rammed onto a stake. It was reasonably fresh and tempting, but he had not survived sixteen years by taking poisoned baits. His own parents, when they had taught him forest lore, had warned against eating meat he had not killed himself. He sprayed the bait, then scornfully scratched a shower of dirt and gravel over it. Let some grovelling hound find it!

He approached the sheep from downwind. Inching forward on his stomach, he chose his prey, a young lamb huddled against its mother in the nearest group. The lamb was small and probably still wobbly on its feet. Even if he sprang too soon, it would be an easy catch.

A barely-audible growl rose in his throat as he bounded forward and snatched the surprised animal. Both ewe and lamb set up a terrified bleating. The other sheep leaped to their feet, baa-ing and butting and bumping one another in a frenzied stampede over the ridge. He sank his teeth into the lamb.

He had already turned toward the forest when he heard the dog charging down on him. He dropped his kill and turned to face the challenge, relieved to see only one attacker. He stood his ground until it leaped, then side-stepped and raked his fangs along the dog's ribcage. Whirling, he slashed its shoulder while it was still off balance, sending the lighter animal crashing to the ground. The dog was scrambling to regain its footing when he charged again. This time he seized it by the throat and locked his jaw firmly on its jugular. The dog leaped and jerked and squirmed, its angry snarling fading to a fearful, panting moan, but he held tight. Finally, its eyes began to glaze and the struggling stopped. He tossed its carcass to the ground and kicked dirt on it.

A boy stood silhouetted on the ridge, small and black in the evening haze. He was armed with only a staff and kept his distance. "Lupo! Il Lupo! Lupaccio!" he began to shout. His cry was echoed by deeper male voices in the distance, and the tocsin rang from the camponile of the cathedral.

The wolf retrieved his prize and carried it by its slender neck into the trees. Doubling back along his trail through the meadow and oaks, he climbed gradually into a forest of gray-green pines until he reached the entrance to his cave, a fissure in the side of a marble cliff. Finally he could rest—and feast.

He relished the taste of sheep, especially the tender flesh of lamb. The pungent flavor was a welcome change from the gamy tastes he had survived on for so many years. His hunger increased his enjoyment and when he finished a short while later, only the largest bones were left.

He felt lazy now, sated by his meal, and dragged himself into his den. The scents and memories of years greeted him, the many litters he and his mate had raised, the spring nights they had raced pell-mell down the mountain face, snapping and nipping at one another in their love-play, howling to each other across the windy ridges, revelling in their youth and strength—and in their bond, severed by the townsmen of Gubbio.

Again he walked to the cave entrance. He pointed his snout toward the moon rising in the southeast and, like the apotheosis of all man's primitive fears, howled one long, desolate wail down toward the city.

*That* for your chants and bells and cowardly hounds!

# 2

# Francesco

His first reaction, when he heard the voices approaching, was to scuttle to the darkest corner of his hut, huddling himself into a tight ball like an animal trying to hide from a predator. Two months before, his father had dragged him back to the family house and locked him in the cellar prison. He would still be rattling his manacles in that dampness if his mother had not freed him while his father was away on business.

And just eight days before, Rainuccio di Palmerio, the messenger for the governors of Assisi, had stood outside his door and formally announced, "Francesco di Pietro Bernardone! Be it known to everyone that you, by order of the consuls, are to be accused and tried!" He remained inside until Rainuccio had repeated his cry several times. At last he had emerged into the blinding brightness of the snow-covered courtyard. He squinted as he replied, as steadily as possible, "Your summons does not apply to me. For some time I have been free of every power of the consuls. I am now the servant of the Most High."

9

Legally, he knew he was on firm ground. Since the old priest of San Damiano had officially accepted him as an oblate, a kind of layman-monk without vows, he was no longer under civil jurisdiction. Only the church could judge him now. He also knew his father would persist. Pietro Bernardone would have satisfaction for his stolen merchandise and horse! It would take more than a point of law to hold him at bay!

From his corner he focused on the pathway as footsteps crunched through the snow in his direction. Someone knocked softly.

"Francesco," called the priest. "Would you come out, please? There is another messenger here. From Bishop Guido."

It was a summons he could not refuse. "One moment," he called. He fumbled through a pile of clothes, the clothes he wore when he came to live with the priest. He now preferred the rough serge robe of a hermit, but he still used his squirrel-lined mantle, a soiled and sorry souvenir of its former splendor, as a barrier against the winter cold.

He opened the door, shielding his eyes for a moment while they adjusted to the light. The two poor olive trees in the priest's courtyard were splayed with hoar ice, and he marvelled that renewed life could be gathering under their frigid shrouds.

He knew the messenger, one of the sons of Vivieno. Andreo di Vivieno, he believed. So now he wore the pale blue livery of the bishop. A good beginning to a career! The youth was his junior by a few years, and he recalled that Andreo had idolized him but a few years before.

The boy was clearly uncomfortable in his present summoner's role. He unfurled a scroll as Francesco emerged from the hut and began to read in a quavering voice.

"Francesco di Pietro Bernardone, you are hereby enjoined to present yourself in three days, at the hour of None, at the court

10

of the Bishop Guido, to respond to the accusation made by Pietro, your father, and against it to say and to oppose what you will wish and be able to do."

Francesco moved nearer while the messenger was reading. "Return to the bishop," he said, "and tell him that I will appear as commanded. He is the father and lord of all souls."

The boy seemed relieved that he had not angered Francesco. "I'm sorry," he ventured. "I hope this will settle the quarrel between you and Sior Bernardone once and for all."

Francesco smiled. "Yes, it must be difficult for the families close to our own," he said. "But I think the city as a whole is enjoying the spectacle. Thank you for your good heart, though. I, too, hope my father will finally be willing to leave me in peace."

Andreo bowed and was turning to go when Francesco spoke again. "Do you dance with the Tripudianti this spring? I always felt that you hoped to join us when you were older."

The boy blushed. "I can't, Francesco. Bishop Guido says they are too *intemperate*. It would cost me my position."

Francesco smiled again. "That sounds like our dear bishop. *Temperanza! Moderazione!* The twin themes of all his sermons. He's right about the Tripudianti, though. Their carousing has become far too wild. The warm evenings of May, strong wine, eager nymphs—a dangerous combination for a young man like yourself. I'm embarrassed when I think I once led their revels."

The priest, who had waited to one side during the formalities, now rejoined them. *"Padre,"* Francesco said, "do you recall how Bishop Guido warned me against intemperance when I joined you here? 'Even asceticism can be carried to the extreme.' I still hear his words, every time

I'm tempted to stuff a little more straw into my mattress."

"So do you put the straw in, or leave it out?" Andreo asked.

Francesco patted his shoulder. "Let me put it this way. My father is the wealthiest merchant in Assisi. Perhaps the only man in the city who has more money and property is our bishop. Now you tell me, can such a man counsel wisely against aceticism? If this poor *padre* here, who barely has enough to eat and wear, whose church is in shambles, yet rightly refuses the money I offer him—if this man tells me I have gone too far in imitating Christ's poverty—then I must believe it.

"And speaking of money, you must excuse me now. I have to find a pouch that belongs to Sior Bernardone. Assure Bishop Guido that in three days my father shall have all his wealth safely in his vaults again."

On the third morning, just before noon, he changed his clothing—as meticulously as a knight preparing for battle. He folded his serge robe and placed it purposefully on the table. Today, for one last day, he would be the dutiful son of Bernardone. He would wear only those clothes his father had given him.

First, he slipped the chainsil sherte over his head. The neck, cuffs, and hem around his knees were all embroidered in the French fashion. His father had always admired the French and, not surprisingly, Francesco's mother was a daughter of Provence.

Over his sherte, Francesco fitted his woven damask bliaut, a tight-fitting tunic laced up both sides. He recalled how some of his former friends in the Tripudianti had worn corsets under their bliauts to improve their figures. The corsets had *not* helped their dancing.

His stockings were made of fine wool and gartered at the thigh, unlike peasants' baggy stockings that had to be cross-gartered all the way up the leg. His shoes, after the fashion of Count Fulk of Anjou, were pointed and curled like a scorpion's sting. Finally (and most importantly to his father), he strapped his leather gripsere with its pouch-full of coins crosswise over his body.

After repeating the canonical psalms for the hour of Sext, he placed his borrowed prayerbook on the hermit's robe and prepared to go. He knew already that he would not return to San Damiano that day, and perhaps never again. He put on the last piece of clothing that could be traced to Pietro Bernardone, the fur-lined hooded mantle with its dangling liripipe, and left the little hut that had been his refuge the past year. He did not seek out the priest, but turned stoically toward Assisi.

It was clearly God's will that Sior Bernardone's money not be used to repair San Damiano. He had been reckless to take the scarlet from his father's shop and sell it, along with the horse that carried the bolts of cloth. Bishop Guido had been right this time! He *had* acted too impulsively!

But when he had knelt in the crumbling church the night before and heard the crucifix, with the gilt chipping from Christ's halo, calling out to him, "Francesco, restore my church, which is falling into ruin"—what could he do but act, and act in the way best known to him? Money had always solved his problems before.

13

Pietro had not reacted well. His son learned quickly the difference between a denier dropped noisily into the money box at Sunday Mass and a bag bulging with silver offered inconspicuously to a poor country priest.

Francesco patted the leather pouch under his mantle. He thought what fun it would be to scatter Pietro's coins like bean seeds in the snow-covered fields where the peasants would find them during the spring plowing.

He was still chuckling when he caught up with a man stooped under a bundle of kindling. Francesco recognized him at once—Lorenzo, the gardener at Moiano, the manor adjoining the bishop's palace. He had a reputation for piety and simplicity, and Francesco was gladdened by the meeting.

He carried the old man's load to the city walls; Lorenzo listened, in turn, while Francesco talked of his summons to appear before the bishop.

"You are right to give back the money," Lorenzo said at last. "Let Caesar keep what is his. If you truly mean to follow God, you must rely only on Him and no longer on your family. Remember how the lilies of the field were clothed."

Francesco looked at the threadbare, torn cape that served as the gardener's main protection against the cold.

"And is your cape a sample of the way God clothes those He loves?" He asked the question affectionately, for he knew and welcomed the answer.

"It is enough," Lorenzo said. "It will see me through this winter, and when I need another, God will provide once again."

"If I traded cloaks with you right now, would you accept it as God's gift?"

"Thank you, no, Francesco. The mantle you wear came from Sior Bernardone. It is his, as surely as the money you carry is his."

Francesco laughed, his face suddenly as radiant as the white countryside.

"You're right, Lorenzo. You're absolutely right!"

# 3

## Troubadour

The wife of Bresco the tailor craned her neck, stretched on tiptoes, tried to pull herself up on her husband's shoulders—all to no avail.

"What's happening?" she whispered, for the crowd in front of her had suddenly hushed, sucking in the cold air as one body. Even Bishop Guido, whom she *could* see, had risen from his throne at the top of the stairs, a look of shock and pain on his face.

"What's the boy *doing?*" she tugged urgently. Some in the crowd had started to titter, and a few of the nobles watching from their balconies were grinning uneasily.

"I can't tell for sure," Bresco said. "I think he's taking off all his clothes."

The bishop had already started down the steps, fumbling at the gold clasps of his cloak, as Francesco piled his clothing at his father's feet. Pietro Bernardone scooped them up quickly, flushing with confusion. He, the great merchant, *reipublicae benefactor et provisor,* by this single gesture of his son, had been cast in the role of a niggardly, stonehearted parent. All he had wanted was justice!

Francesco stretched out his arms to the snowflakes drifting into the piazza. They brushed his bare skin, cool and delicate as the kisses of angels. He glanced again at the old man, savoring the completeness of his freedom and his total triumph in this, their final quarrel. He reddened himself, however, when he saw the humiliation in his father's eyes. He tried to back away, but Bishop Guido swiftly enveloped him in his velvet cloak.

No retreat! Father before, bishop behind. He had to finish the drama as he rehearsed it in his mind since meeting Lorenzo on the road. He turned from both men and fronted the audience. His voice was strong and lyrical as he spoke.

"Until this day, I have called Pietro Bernardone my father, but here I give him back his money and even the clothing that I have had of him. In the future, I shall only say, 'Our Father, Who art in Heaven.'"

When he turned again, Sior Bernardone was gone. The bishop, too, was retreating up the stairs to his palace. Only the spectators watched as he fell silent and began examining the blue, ermine-lined mantle that hung loosely around his thin shoulders.

"Too fine," he said to the closest in the crowd. "It's too fine. Won't one of you trade with me? A patched old smock or cape for this fine cloak?"

The crowd now began to mock openly. With the bishop and the rich merchant gone, they could taunt freely this crazy youth who had become

18

their favorite laughingstock the past few months. A hand reached out and pushed him and another grabbed his cloak.

"Hey, Francesco, where do you find poppy juice in the dead of winter?" someone called from a balcony.

"Dog's brain and hemlock, more like it!"

He pulled away and hurried toward the open end of the piazza.

Lorenzo. He would seek out the old gardener at Moiano. God clearly wanted *him* to have the bishop's cloak.

Francesco cleared the piazza in a shower of hoots and snowballs. Even Bresco, at the back of the crowd, lobbed a snowball in his direction and laughed all the harder when it fell short and hit a guildsman he disliked.

The tailor's wife scowled and shoved him as he stooped for more snow, sending him sprawling on the slippery stones.

"Don't pick on the boy! You know his mind hasn't been the same since the Perugians captured him."

Bresco sat up, still cackling, but the woman wasn't done.

"How's he supposed to survive with no food or money and just a cloak against this cold? His poor mother! Pica must be breaking her heart!"

She pulled on his arm as her husband struggled to his feet.

"Let's go in, father. I'm getting the chills just thinking about him."

By the time the coals were building in the tailor's fireplace, the former son of Bernardone was climbing the steep ox-cart road outside the city walls, his feet already numb on the frozen mud. At the peak of the Nocigliano Heights, frost began to form on his scraggly beard and his eyelashes were freezing together. He should have felt miserable, but he only had a calm sense of something that was done and something that was about to begin.

As he entered the oak forest cresting the road he burst abruptly into song—not a Latin dirge of the church, or even a plaintive local folk song, but a love ballad from Provence that he had learned from a wandering *jongleur* years before.

Qant li rossignols s'es crie,
Qui nod desduit de son chant,
Por ma belle dolce amie,
Vois mon cuer rossignolant.
Jointes mains merci li crie,
Car onques rien n'amai tant
Et bien sai, s'elle m'oblie,
Que joie me va finant…
Chascuns dit que je foloi,
Mais nuns nel set mieuz de moi.

When the nightingale sings
Who charms us with his song,
For my fair sweet love
My heart also sings like a bird.
With joined hands I beg her mercy,
For never have I loved so much.
I know well that, should she banish me,
It would be the end of my joy…
Everyone says I'm a fool,
But no man knows better than I.

The song honored the elegant Eleanor, the Lady of Aquataine, the onetime Queen of both England and France. But in Francesco's mind another maiden reigned, a plain girl in rags who had often invaded his sleep and whom he could now, finally, think of as his own. If his fantasies had once bubbled with the effervescence of courtly life, the airy, faerie life of knights and balladeers (in contrast to his mundane cloth-merchant's role), he now saw himself as the minstrel of King Christ and the tatter-demalion knight of Lady Poverty. He had at last snapped every silken cord and family bond that had kept him from chasing headlong after his latest cause. And in the pure joy of freedom, he sang.

He disappeared into the ice-rimed woods clothed only in the gardener's cape, without a scrap of food, without family or job or plan, or even a real destination. He was simply following the road. It did occur to him that the road led eventually to Gubbio, a city where he would be welcome. Gubbio had joined armies with Assisi in their last war against Perugia. Perhaps there he could find work and pursue his new life in anonymity and quiet.

He could not imagine, at this stage, what feats his Lady would set to prove his valor. He knew only that she would forge him in the Christ-mold, and that image both terrified and challenged him—a Being of total humility, a poor Wanderer relying for food and shelter on the whim of strangers, the Son of an insatiable Father Who demanded ever more excruciating sacrifices: an abject figure, beaten and abused, His head lacerated with thorns, palms and feet bleeding tortuously...

Mostly he feared the loneliness of Christ, he who once had thrived on the adulation of friends. He shuddered when he realized he had taken only the first step in the imitation of his King, though he had already left behind everything he had ever known.

He had just passed a tiny country church, dropping down toward the Porziano crossroad, when he saw the outline of a man round the curve ahead. The brush stirred behind him as two more men stepped out onto

the road. Instinct caused him to recoil, perhaps some memory of his moldy Perugian prison. He knew that Perugia paid retainers to extort tolls from travelers in this northwest district of Assisi Commune. He had no possessions to lose, but still his legs stiffened, even when his brain reminded him that he had given himself entirely into God's hands.

"May the Lord grant you peace and good," he said when he could make out the first man's features.

"Better you should wish us prosperity, little man," the stranger replied. His voice was flat and humorless. "Who are you, and what do you carry?"

"I am the Troubadour of the Great King," he replied.

"Aaah. Then you must be well provisioned."

"I am provisioned with infinite love. A man needs no more."

The leader was now close enough to scrutinize him. He looked contemptuously at the coarse woolen cape.

"If you are a troubadour, then I am the angel Gabriel. I'd say you were the buffoon of a great idiot!" He yanked off the cape, only then spotting the "crusader's" cross Francesco had chalked on the back.

"He's bare-assed as a babe!" said one of the men behind him.

"And cracked as a gourd!"

The leader was looking at the cross. Then he threw the cape to the ground, muttering something about lice, and glared into the naked man's dark eyes.

"Cracked on religion, are you?" he said. "That gains you no favors here. Had you a half-denier or a pouch of food, you might have escaped a beating."

"My Lord was scourged, though He had done no wrong." Francesco mumbled the words, as if for his own benefit, steadying his mind for what must follow. His Lady had set this task so suddenly that he was barely prepared.

The gang's chief hit him first, catching him with his fist flush on a cheekbone. Almost simultaneously, a cudgel cracked against his ribs from behind while another struck his lower spine. He stumbled toward the edge of the road where it dropped off into a wide valley, and as he fell forward a fourth blow grazed the back of his head, sending him tumbling down the hillside. He landed face down in a snow bank, his skull flashing with bright orange and red and yellow lights exploding one inside another.

He heard the robbers guffawing from the road as he lay in the snow. "There's a proper bed for a fool herald," one called down to him. "Sleep there, you hick buffoon!"

He did not move for several minutes, until the voices above him had drifted away. Then he tottered to his feet and climbed back up to the road. He retrieved his cape and set out limping, down toward the fields on the valley floor. Now at least he had an immediate destination. With the monks of Valfabbrica, he would be safe for the night.

His skin, as he hobbled out of the woods, had faded from its usual olive color to a chill pink. His body throbbed, but his mind was exhilarated, and he was surprised by the impulse to sing again. He had now added physical suffering to the jeering at Bishop Guido's palace. He had survived the first two steps on his new path and each step had deepened his understanding of his agonized Lord.

"I am the Troubadour…of the Great King," he intoned across the amphitheater of the valley.

# 4

## Poverello

An icy darkness had already crystallized around the monastery-stronghold of Santa Maria di Valfabbrica by the time he pounded on the gate. Dark clouds buffeted the moon from the southwest, portending snow or rain or hail. What moonlight there was gave the surrounding fields an endless, out-of-time quality—grey and featureless as some eternal void.

The oak door of the monastery seemed more apt for a military fortress with its tiny peephole and slots for protruding weapons. The Benedictines who lived there were better known as warriors than as men of prayer. Landlords of the neighboring castles and farms, they were hard hit by the raids of the local warlords. Perugian bands led by the sons of Monaldo and Suppolino would plunder the outlying fiefs, murdering the farmers and salting their fields. Periodically, they would seize the castles nearest the border and the monks would charge out in full battle gear to recapture their holdings and restore the serfs' allegiance to themselves.

A single taper above the monastery entrance glared at the traveler as he knocked again. He waited nearly fifteen minutes before the peephole squeaked open.

"Who's there?" the brother porter demanded. He was clearly irritated at the late arrival.

"Only a poor servant of the Lord."

"Only a lazy beggar looking for a handout, you mean."

Francesco said nothing, but stood patiently. He knew the rule of St. Benedict required them to take him in. Finally he heard the scraping of chains and locks, and the door opened enough for him to slip through.

The two monks who escorted him down the dark corridor to the refectory looked skeptically at the ragged guest.

"Do you believe that Jesus is the Son of God?" one of them asked suddenly. His tone was hostile.

"Yes. Most firmly."

"Is your allegiance to Pope or empire?"

"The holy Innocent is my spiritual father on earth."

The monks seemed satisfied for the moment, though still disgusted with their charge.

"You look like a sodomite son of Waldo or one of the Patarini. Do you sympathize with the Patarini?"

"The church will always be my mother."

Francesco was familiar with the religious offshoots that had sprouted all over Europe in recent years—Waldensians, Albigensians, Cathari. They dressed in tatters and preached poverty and renunciation, denouncing the Pope and his hierarchy (as well as the monasteries) for their links with "the princes of this world." One sect, the Patarini, had ejected wealthy bishops from cities north of Tuscany. Pope Innocent III retaliated by branding the reformers "heretics," and the Inquisitors' stakes were already flaming from Italy to Spain.

A heap of vermillion embers glowed against the traveler as the procession passed through the refectory to a straw pallet in the far corner, well-removed from the fire and the monks' dining tables.

"Sit there, good-for-naught. I'll find you some bread and drink."

"God bless you," Francesco answered, grateful for a place to rest.

The brother-of-the-many-questions soon returned and challenged him again.

"Where is your home, and what is your Christian name?"

27

"I have no home," he answered. His expression had become abstracted. "I suppose I don't have a name anymore either. Just this morning I returned to Sior Bernardone everything he had ever given me. That must mean my name, too, don't you think?"

The second monk tapped his temple. "Call him what he is, a little beggar," he said.

"Little beggar. *Poverello*. It suits him."

A muffled hymn drifted into the refectory from the basilica where the rest of the community was gathered. The chant sweetened the coarse rye bread in his mouth as though it had been spread with honey.

Poverello. The Little Poor Man. It did more than suit him. It was the perfect title for the errant knight of Lady Poverty.


During the night he dreamed a great wave had crashed against the monastery of Valfabbrica, sucking its massive walls stone by stone into a turbulent sea. He woke, shivering. He never knew when his dreams were God-inspired or contained a clue to action. The recent changes in his life that had so mystified his friends and enraged his father had all begun with some dream or vision.

What if he really were insane? What if he really had thrown his life away at the beck of an overly-vivid imagination?

He knelt on the straw pallet and began to pray.

"I trust You, my Lord, to guide my steps truly. Please forgive any *lack* of trust in me. Please make my trust complete."

A bleak aura still spread from the hearth, lighting up the monks' armor and weapons hanging on the refectory walls—shields and helmets, breastplates and gauntlets, pikes, maces, swords and polished crossbows. A heavy rain was now drumming on the tiled roof and he thought he heard shouting outside. At the same time, the chanting began again in the distance. Matins or Prime? In the darkness, he had no notion of the hour.

A lantern entered the opposite end of the refectory and the porter padded across to his bed.

"Awake, Poverello? Good! It will be light soon. Time for you to be gone!"

"Bless you, brother, for your care. Can you tell me how much further it is to Gubbio?"

"Gubbio? I thought you were heading south!"

"No brother. I came from Assisi."

"Then you'd best be a strong swimmer. The Chiagio flooded last night. One of our tenant farmers just told me the Gubbio road runs through a lake now."

The young man lowered his head for a moment.

"May I stay here until the flood subsides? I will work for my food, most willingly."

The monk groaned.

"The Scriptures are right. You poor will *always* be with us. All right! Follow me! You want work? You'll have plenty!"

He led Francesco into the next hall, the scullery, where two more monks were preparing the community's breakfast. They moved about like chiaroscuro figures in the light of the baking oven. A large cauldron,

29

smelling wonderfully of hot barley, hung in another fireplace while a jug of milk sat warming nearby.

"What have you brought us now, Milo?" said the head cook, glancing up from the bread he was slicing. "You don't expect me to fatten *that* up, do you?"

"Just put him to work, and feed him what you will," the porter said. "We're stuck with him for a few days."

The cook eyed him with the same disdain the porter had shown. Finally, he cut a crust from the end of a loaf and scraped it toward Francesco with his knife.

"Take this before you faint. Then you can start splitting firewood."

He thanked the cook and took the bread. He looked hopefully at an open kettle on the cutting table. Tiny islands of coagulated grease floated on the surface of a cold broth, probably left over from the previous evening.

"Don't be dipping your bread in there," the cook growled. "That's for the pigs, not for the likes of you."

He chewed down the dry bread and went out into the rain. As he left, he saw another monk driving a serf toward an open gate, cursing and beating him with a long pole.

"Three of our swine are drowned in the river while you slept?... And how are you to repay us? With paving stones? Just get out, I tell you! And don't hope to herd for us again!... God's blood and the blood of the swine be on your worthless head!"

The tenant, who had been trying to plead his cause, saw that escape was his only real recourse and darted through the gate. The monk shook his stick one last time and crossed the farmyard, glowering at Francesco as they passed.

"What are you doing here?" he asked.

"Brother cook sent me to split firewood," Francesco replied.

"Then get to it, before you get the same as that piece of dung who just left."

The woodshed, fortunately, was under cover—a long open structure with a roof but no walls. He began splitting logs, using a crude mallet formed from a chunk of hardwood with an iron bar forced through its midsection as the handle. Within minutes, his palms began to burn from the friction of the metal. Blisters welted up and finally popped. He turned

31

to the thinner branches, snapping them into kindling across his knee. The rough bark was a harsh contrast to the slippery silks and soft cottons he was used to handling in his father's shop.

By the time he had finished in the woodshed, the monks had finished their morning collation and he was pointed to a pile of tin plates and mugs. The hot dishwater seared his blisters and he thought of the wounds in the palms of his crucified Lord.

That day led into the next as the dishwashing led into slopping the hogs, scrubbing vegetables, sweeping the scullery and refectory, washing the dining tables, gathering eggs, tending the fires. The cook's attitude toward him softened when he saw that the Poverello tackled all his chores with good cheer and made no demands in return. At one point the monk even offered him a mug of hot wine, but the young man refused him graciously.

"It would please my tongue too much, brother. And who knows what stronger desire might proceed from this brief pleasure? Your tasty mug could be the first link in the chain that drags me down to hell."

As his stay dragged on, his chores took on the nature of ritual and his meals even more so. Prior Ugo and his subprior would take their seats first at the head of the "U" formed by the long trestle tables. The other monks would then settle on the benches flanking the tables while the cook and his helpers brought in the food. The monastery hounds milled in the open area of the "U," waiting for scraps. The lector of the week, seated on a dais near the fireplace, tried to make himself heard above the clamor of the eating monks.

When the meal had been served, Francesco would withdraw to his straw pallet and wait, lulled by the drone of the lector's voice as he read the biography of some Benedictine saint.

"Hey, Poverello! Catch!" one of the monks would suddenly call and a bit of food would fly in his direction. The dogs knew the itinerant-beggar game well and would race to get to the scrap first. Strangely enough, Francesco enjoyed the game too, and was content to retrieve a little bread and an occasional olive or piece of cheese. The rest he relinquished to the animals, his brother beggars.

When the meal was over, the tables were tipped on their trestles and the refectory became a bedlam of clattering tin, cheering monks and yapping hounds. Francesco sat quietly in his corner, waiting until the dogs had had their fill. Then he righted the tables, gathered the plates and mugs, and began his round of cleaning chores again.

# 5

# Asino

One day, near the end of March, the warming wind blowing from the southwest brought no rain. The sun trumpeted the arrival of spring and the porter brought word that the Chiagio was back within its banks. The Poverello could resume his pilgrimage.

He left Valfabbrica like a man reprieved from a suffocating room. Not that the air inside the monastery walls was more stifling than that he now inhaled so gustily. The torpor of Valfabbrica was a different sort. It drifted on the monks' conversations as the smoke drifted from the leaky chimney cowl in the refectory. There the community gathered for talk and warmth each evening. And the Poverello, listening from his corner, would be drawn against his will back to the shop of Pietro Bernardone.

Because his father was the richest of Assisi's merchants, the others looked to him for guidance and reassurance. They would tag along behind him as he sorted among his bales of damasks and embroidered samite, reveling in the bankruptcy of the estate owners whose lands were transferring steadily into the hands of the banker-merchants—or reviling the *castellans,* those tower-dwelling remnants of feudal society who still extracted tolls from the merchants crossing their roads to reach markets or newly-acquired properties.

The monks' concerns echoed all the greed and bitterness of his father's friends: quarrels over tithes and jurisdictions, feudal and ecclesiastical enmities, Perugia and her constables. They especially delighted in fantasizing tortures for these tax collectors.

"They should be blinded and mutilated like Tancred's son."

"The jailers in Salerno have the right idea. They saw their enemies in half. Send them back to Perugia in baskets, I say!"

"In Milan, they tie prisoners' hands behind their backs. Then they wrap their hands in straw and set the straw on fire."

"Ho! That would keep their grubby fingers out of our purses!"

*And what have monks to do with property and purses?* Francesco reflected as he walked along the Chiagio. He was glad now that he had resisted Bishop Guido's urgings.

Back in the first days of his conversion, when he dressed like an ascetic and spent hours praying in caves and abandoned churches, the bishop had called him to his palace.

"Francesco," he warned, "I know your piety is sincere, but I must question your seclusion. You have no experience in spiritual matters. Take the advice of an old man, one who has served God through three of

35

your lifetimes. Join a religious order! Subject your youth and impetuosity to the discipline of a holy rule! Be certain that your religious impulse comes from God and not from Satan."

He could only hope that his inspiration was, in fact, from God. One thing he could say for certain: his *expiration* as he left the monastery was a sigh of relief. Once again his freedom had been affirmed. He had escaped Santa Maria di Valfabbrica as he had escaped his father's house and the dungeons of Perugia.

Like his namesake Giovanni Battista (the name his mother had given him before his father returned from France and rechristened him Francesco), he hoped one day to serve as a voice from the wilderness. And like that desert wolf John, he would never become entangled in the affairs of a religious community.

Alluvium and amaryllis—the world of barely spring.

The brown waters of the Chiagio churned through banks of silt and rubble. But the ooze between his toes was warm and the puddles on the road reflected rainbows and taffetas. New greenery vibrated on the poplars lining the river and a distant grove of olive trees was already white with blossoms.

He crossed the old Roman bridge to the paved road on the opposite bank and climbed toward Biscina, the castle that dominated the gorge like the background in a pastoral tapestry. Blood-red poppies flamed across the hillsides, flicking out sparks of golden buttercups and broom, orange marigolds, and feathery white lace.

His feet began to shuffle on the road, recalling an old May dance. Just a year ago he had assembled his company for their first rehearsals. But this spring, another young man would lead the revels, intoning the songs of love and reborn life, mocking fusty and jealous husbands:

36

Mas pir reient la far, eya!
K'ele n'a soing de viellart, eya!
Mais d'un legier bachelar, eya!
Ki ben sache sola car!

But our sweetest lady here, eya!
Has of old men little care, eya!
And for lightsome bachelors, eya!
Keeps she that heart of hers!

And would they in their gambols ask of him, their abdicated king? Would some tender female heart sigh just once, "Ah, it's just not the same without Francesco"? He had surrendered more than his birthright when he left Assisi, more than just his natural family. So many close companions, the friends of his entire life.

But as he paused and looked back at the river far below, the towers of Valfabbrica, the castle of Coccarano, the panoply of spring flora, he realized that he had lost nothing. Here was the world in all its beauty and youth, strength and age, spread beneath his feet. He had merely made God the trustee of all that he had. And now that he had nothing, he could see everything for what it truly was—a divine gift. Pleasurable or unpleasant, the entire world was now on loan to him, and he was overwhelmed with gratitude.

"Praise to You, Lord, for all You have created!" he shouted. The cliffs repeated his hymn.

"I love You!" he sang out and again the gorge replied. He laughed aloud, like a delighted child, then resumed his climb. The path grew steep and narrow, passing through small wooded copses and fenced crofts. Finally he reached the high road linking Perugia and Gubbio.

There on the ridge of the Gualdo Mountains he could see all the way back to Assisi. Suspended between Mount Subasio and the Tiber Valley, his former home hung like a translucent pendant on a backdrop of green felt, the pink- and coral-marbled petals of the distant cathedral, walls and towers infused with sunlight.

Pietro Bernardone owned much of that greensward surrounding the city. Poor Pietro! All that empire and no Francesco to guard and enlarge it.

Gubbio was a dun-colored, umber city, he recalled from woolen-buying expeditions—as austere in appearance and spirit as its sister to the south was roseate and warm. But Gubbio was his future, and his view in that direction expanded with each step along the mountain crest.

The fields flanking the summit were hedged not with fences, but with barriers of tangled blackberry vines. Occasionally a side path would cut through the briers, off toward a farm tower or castle clinging to a mountain spur. It was from one of these trails that the two young women emerged.

At first they froze in their tracks, waiting to hear if he carried the warning clapper of a leper or seemed in any way dangerous. Satisfied that he was only an unarmed beggar, they continued toward him.

Like him, they were obviously heady with the mulled wine of spring. Both were brightly dressed. The smaller of the two, who seemed about sixteen, wore a full-length bliaut over her dark chemise. Her head was encircled by a gold virgin's crown from which her hair twisted in a single plait. She was not pretty. Her face seemed permanently flushed and her forehead and cheeks were blemished, but there was a shyness about her that appealed to his own.

The other woman, a few years older, was large and soft-fleshed. Her hips rocked casually beneath her skirt and her full breasts stretched the fabric of her short surcoat. Her eyes, and the ringlets dangling from her white headdress, were black as his own. The curls jounced as she curtsied playfully toward him.

"Sior beggar, I see you are out surveying your domain this afternoon. If you will be kind to us, we might let you survey our picnic basket as well."

Francesco stiffened as she crossed to his side of the road. His confusion only added to the woman's amusement.

"Lucia, come see! He's rather handsome if you can look beyond the dirt."

She extended the basket toward him and curtsied. "Wouldn't you like some treat from us, my lord?"

He tried to slip past her, but he was cornered against the edge of the road. Over the woman's shoulder he could see her timorous friend walking slowly toward him.

"I think he's a mute, Lucia. Shouldn't we take him home? He could never carry tales on us."

The woman scanned his slight frame and the thin ankles protruding beneath the hem of his cloak. "On second thought he's probably too small for me. Yes, I would definitely have to throw him back. I surrender him to you! You two could grapple rather equally, I should think."

The younger girl's whole body seemed to blush at her friend's temerity. Yet as her eyes caught his, he saw that her embarassment was mingled with attraction. They were the soft brown yearning eyes of a yearling doe.

Near the arbor of Loncpré
I was wandering yesterday.
There I saw, moving tremulously,
A maid pleasant and young and pretty.
God, I was enraptured, to see her all alone,
Singing to herself, a plaintive and pleading song,
"Robin, I should be loved.
You risk much to wait too long."

The look was a plea for comfort and understanding, and something basic and male within him wanted to reach out to her. His emotions hitched and strained, like a dancer caught in a melancholy phrase. He bolted between the two women and began running as hard as he could. Laughter bounded close behind him, over a dip in the road, pushing him faster and faster until he outdistanced it at last. Pain, sharp as flint, jabbed at his ribcage and pebbles half-buried in the muddy road bruised his bare soles.

Finally he slowed to a gasping walk, but his stride was still energetic as he began berating himself.

"*Stolto*! You dunce of an idiot! Brother flesh...must you still behave like some breeding, braying Sicilian donkey? *Fra Asino*...that's you! Brother Ass...must I beat you and starve the stubbornness out of you?"

He flung off his cloak and plunged his naked body into a thick patch of blackberry runners, losing his footing as he slid down into the thorns.

"You will learn, Fra Asino!" he yelled as the briers pricked and pulled and ripped his skin. He twisted and rolled and turned until he felt the shy Lucia was completely purged from his desires. At last, with blood trickling from a hundred tiny wounds, he crawled back onto the road. He began scraping with his fingernails in the mud, forming a row of little mounds alongside his cloak.

"What do you want, Brother Ass?" he cried as he poked at the piles of mud. "Here! Here, Francesco Bernardone! Here is your wife. Here are your four children. Here are your maidservant and your manservant. Now go! Find yourself two jobs, for they are all hungry and crying for food. Is this what you want, Francesco?

"Or is your cloak enough? Do you want family, friends and servants, or to serve the One Master? Decide! Are you still Francesco Bernardone or are you the Poverello? Decide now and live forever with your choice!"

41

He buried his face in his muddy palms, his aching body pulsing and twitching as he sobbed out his loneliness.

Slowly, one hand stretched out toward the ragged cloak and pulled it around his shoulders. He lurched to his feet and stumbled on toward Gubbio.

# 6

## La Caccia

Deep in wolf dreams, he was unaware the earth had revolved to mid-afternoon. He slept heavily, snuffling in the stale odors of his cave, snoring noisily as he exhaled, point and counterpoint, in a drowsy dance lasting half a day. He had not been gorged so in months.

The previous afternoon, he had spied from his woods as a white ox calf had meandered from its pasture and in among the trees. Its mother, with another of the oxen, had been yoked and led down to the fields below the city where spring plowing had begun. And the calf, ignored for the moment, had strayed in search of richer forage. It had even stumbled on the wolf's favorite trail, followed it to the clearing, and there, with its nose buried in a clump of wild rye grass, the calf had heard the predator too late. With the wolf riding its shoulders, it had staggered as far as the

meadow's edge before it went down, hemorrhaging from the neck, immobilized by fright and panic, burdened by the 130 pounds gnawing at its spine.

Had he known that the people of the city considered their cream-colored, heavy-humped oxen sacred, the wolf might have overlooked this windfall and continued hunting for safer prey. More likely, given his contempt for the humans, the result would have been the same. He devoured his kill with gusto, ripping off large chunks of meat and swallowing it whole, savoring the hot blood, the tender muscles and sweet fat of the young animal. For hours he had stretched beside the carcass until, sated at last, he had climbed again to his home, his bloated stomach heavy as a stone.

Normally he stayed alert to any hint of danger, even when he slept. He often curled outside his den where his nose, as well as his ears, could warn him of encroachers in his range. But this night he had crawled the full length of his tunnel to the larger chamber within and slumped into oblivion. Distant canine whining mingled with his dreams of blind newborn pups, pushing and mewling as they pressed upon their mother's teats. Even the shout of human voices only conjured scenes of angry herdsmen—until they were so close his mind flashed abruptly to his mate's final violent stand, the hounds in a snarling semicircle, the men closing in as she clawed and leaped against the sheer wall, nowhere to run, jabbed and slashed and battered to lifeless carrion. He snapped awake and scrambled up the passage.

Too late! A pack of men and dogs had tracked him to his den. The animals charged as he emerged. He retreated back down the tunnel a few feet, where they would have to come at him one at a time. Beyond the dogs he saw the men approaching armed with pikes and maces—and torches. He could not defend himself in the cave. He once discovered a sooty den, still reeking of smoke. Inside, four wolves lay dead, unscarred, as if they had merely failed to waken from sleep. Not he! If his time to die had come, he would at least have the wounds of his killers for his memorial.

The hair bristled along the scruff of his neck and around the scent gland at the base of his tail. He bared his teeth and rushed growling into the sunlight. He caught the nearest dog by a foreleg and would have crushed the slender bones. But he had to whirl and chase another dog who slashed at his flank. A third charged against his shoulder but was thrown off by the sheer weight of the wolf. He twisted and leaped, biting and snapping, trying to break the circle.

An impatient hunter waded into the melee and raised his mace. The wolf jumped aside, felt a sharp spike slice across his ribs. The man raised his club again and this time the wolf leaped straight for his arm.

The hunter's hide and muscles were as soft as a fish's belly and opened easily to his fangs, clean to the bone. The man screamed and dropped his weapon. As he jerked away, the wolf vaulted off his back, using it like a springboard to clear the ring of attackers. A pike bounced off the wall above him and another grazed his tail. The dogs seemed momentarily stunned as the man tumbled face-down among them. Then they set out baying in pursuit.

The wolf headed not for the trees, but higher up the mountain. His body ached, and he knew he lacked the speed of the pack leaders, but their hesitation had given him the head start he needed. On the open hillside his main strength, his endurance, would work to his advantage. The dogs had also spent the day climbing to his den while he was resting.

45

The mountains in his range were a series of broken canyons and crags, of barely visible ledges criss-crossing the steep walls and gorges. For more than an hour he loped and leaped and scrambled up and down the rocky hillsides while the howling behind him grew gradually fainter. The pack was spreading out and only two or three of the hounds were still seriously in the chase.

He forced himself onward, switching back in the general direction of Gubbio, running along the crest of the mountain now. The walled city in the distance looked smaller than his paw.

He pressed for several more miles, glancing back at his pursuers scattered across the face of the mountain. The leader was about two hundred yards behind him; the others straggled at wide intervals far below.

He turned and waited, grey and hard as a statue in the deepening blue evening. He snapped up a mouthful of snow to slake his thirst as he watched the dogs advance.

They would come to him now, singly as he had planned. He knew he could never again return to the cave that had been home to his mate and him, but her death would at last be avenged.

The lead dog panted toward him, its tongue flopping with exhaustion, and the full fury of the old warrior hurtled down upon it.

7

# Spadalunga

Giacomello Spada stormed through the alley connecting the Piazza di San Lorenzo with the main Piazza del Mercato. His brothers and bodyguards swirled in the wake of his furious strides as the alley opened into the marketplace.

He stopped and turned abruptly, as if addressing a corps of horsemen, and grabbed the hilt of his famous long sword.

"The little jackrabbit escaped me this time, but if I ever see him in our quarter again, armed or unarmed, I swear I'll skewer him on this blade."

"You can't keep him from coming to market," his brother Federigo pointed out. "Even though it's but a bow shot from our homes, the market is public ground."

Antonio, the youngest of the Spada brothers, agreed. "If he doesn't see her here, they'll see each other at Sunday Mass. What's the harm if they roll their eyes at each other from a hundred paces? It's spring, man—and it will pass. We all remember how it feels to be fifteen.

"Granted!" said Giacomello. "But not *him!* No son of Marzialle is going to lust for my niece and live to joke about it. Have you forsaken all pride, Antonio?"

"Giacomello, you're the head of the family, but she's my daughter and I tell you I'm not worried. I'll talk to her again. More seriously this time, I promise you."

Antonio spread his hands in a placating gesture and shrugged to the simmering giant who had refused all his life to reconcile to peace. Antonio felt that his brother should be sitting with the communal consul, harvesting the fruits of his years of military leadership, his grey hair accentuating his noble lineage. Instead, it framed an oft-broken nose that jutted like some rough outcropping from the scarred terrain of his face. And always, always, looking for new battles. If not the Norman invaders to the south, then the Perugians. If not the Perugians, then some family on the north side of Gubbio.

Giacomello was about to object when a noisy mob entered from the opposite end of the piazza. A hooded beggar was moving toward the fountain in the center of the square, slowly and inexorably as a glacier wedging a rabble of screaming urchins and barking dogs from its path.

"*Pazzo! Pazzo!* We've caught a madman!" the children cried. Some of them threw mud and stones, hitting each other in the crossfire as often as they hit the beggar, but still the man moved on, seemingly unaware of

48

the clamor. As he drew nearer, the onlookers could hear him talking in a low voice.

"Yes, that's right. Teach Brother Ass how he must be treated. Every stone earns you a blessing."

The hecklers were within their rights. The laws of the city lumped beggars under the same guidelines, or lack of guidelines, as lepers caught within the walls. Basically, they were at the mercy of the people.

The three brothers watched in silence as the man reached the fountain and began sucking water from his cupped hands and smearing it on his face. A dog dashed in and grabbed the hem of his cape, tearing the fabric as he pulled away. The children howled as the cape split up the back and the beggar tried futilely to cover his nakedness.

"Enough!" Giacomello roared and trampled across the cobble-stones. "Let him alone, or I'll streak all your bottoms with the flat of my sword."

The beggar stood with his head bowed, holding the two halves of his cape together while the boys and girls ran off screeching. When the noise had subsided, he said quietly, "Thank you, Spadalunga, but it was not necessary. They were only helping me to heaven."

Giacomello was startled at the use of his nickname. *Spada*, the "sword," was called *Spadalunga*, "long sword," by his warrior friends. His weapon had become his trademark as much as his huge frame, and both made enemies reluctant to challenge him one-to-one.

"Do I know you?" he asked. He peered into the shadow of the stranger's cowl, at the beard dripping with water, the almond-shaped eyes, and thin lips. The lips parted in a familiar, good-natured grin.

"Bernardone? *Good God,* man, what's happened to you?"

"*God's goodness,* Giacomello. God's limitless goodness."

The hulking nobleman stared down at his former companion, first in disbelief, then disconcertedly as his brothers and retainers gathered around them.

"Antonio. Federigo. I give you Francesco Bernardone," he said.

Now it was the Spada retinue's turn to wonder, puzzled that their head should be on familiar terms, even flustered by this ambulatory heap of rags.

"Francesco's the Assisan I told you about, the merchant's son who fought shoulder-to-shoulder with me at the bridge of San Giovanni. My God, Francesco, you were as fierce as any knight in the field! Even those whoreson Perugians had to respect him. Am I right? Did they not prison you with the *cavalieri* instead of the common soldiers?"

Francesco pulled back his hood and nodded. His friend was speaking all in a rush, gesturing between his brothers and the traveler. Clearly Spadalunga was at a loss to explain the discrepancy between this mud-spattered pilgrim and the exuberant young hero of his war stories. His eyes begged some saving explanation as much as his next remark.

"The last I heard the Perugians had freed you and you were riding south to join the Count Di Brienne."

Francesco responded dreamily, like a man asked to recall some prior lifetime.

"Riding? Yes, it's true. I had my palfrey and war horse. Even a squire. In those days, I wanted only to rise from my class, to win a title like that you were born into. Not buying it, mind you—though my father would

50

willingly have paid the price. I wanted to earn it with my sword and service."

He smiled and played at a rip in his cape. "Our Heavenly Father had other plans for me, though. He led me...well, in a few words, He has led me here, where we meet again."

Antonio had been eyeing the scratches and bruises on the stranger's face. "How can we help you, Sior Bernardone?" he asked. He spoke the title deliberately, to show his respect for the choice Francesco had made.

Francesco seemed to be studying his toes. Impoverishment was a new experience for him. "The monks of Valfabbrica fed me in exchange for work. If you would let me serve in your household, just until I find a regular job..."

"Nonsense!" Giacomello interrupted. "You'll come home with us as an honored guest, and we'll start by clothing you honorably."

He wrapped his arm gingerly around his friend's shoulders and steered him across the piazza. Behind them, from the heart of the city, the tocsin began to clang. Giacomello motioned to a servant who ran off to gather the news at the cathedral.

The houses of the Spada brothers, like many homes of the urban nobility, were built for defense more than for comfort. A constant expectation of assault characterized its construction, from its tall corner towers, to its 18-feet thick stone walls, to its single fortified entrance complete with portcullis and massive oak door. Guards armed with crossbows paced before the elevated gate house and waved down to their masters as the small band approached.

Each brother had a separate dwelling for his family, but all faced the central courtyard with its dominant citadel. The individual homes were

51

linked by enclosed bridges connecting their guard towers above ground and underground tunnels leading to the citadel, the last bastion of defense should the compound come under attack. It held storerooms with provisions sufficient to withstand a six months' siege, kitchens, bread ovens, its own well and latrines, and, as Giacomello observed proudly, a rainwater fishpond on its roof. With care, additional supplies could be smuggled into the citadel through secret tunnels leading outside the city. The south wall of the complex abutted the south wall of the city itself.

A number of smaller buildings filled the gaps between the brothers' houses: the common hall, stables for the nobles' horses, guards' barracks and quarters for menservants, the smith and carpentry shops, and the family chapel. In fact, only one structure lay outside the protecting walls, a large, low building that extended towards the marketplace—an afterthought and an irritation to the eldest brother, Francesco was to learn later.

"Here! You'll look like a prince in this!" Giacomello waved a particolored garment embroidered across the chest with the stanzas of a poem. "And look at this hat!"

The hat was striped in rainbow hues, puffed, pleated, scalloped along the brow, and looked altogether humorous to Francesco. Then he

recalled that he himself had introduced this very fashion into Assisi with great seriousness but a few years earlier.

"*Amico*, you are wonderfully generous. But you do me no favor in trying to resurrect the late peacock of Assisi."

"Oh, come, Francesco. I know you like a favorite story. If anyone has ever idolized the Lady Fashion, it's you."

"And I tell you again, the Author of that story has revised it many times since you read it last. Have you no worn garment, something too shabby to pass down to one of your menservants, perhaps? I would be overjoyed to have such a gift from you."

Spadalunga gazed at him with a trace of disappointment, then began rummaging again through the huge chest at the foot of his bed.

"Here's a tunic I wear for hunting. Grey as a mouse's back and the most wretched thing I own. If my wife knew this were here, she'd have it for cleaning rags."

"It's perfect. Look no further."

They both collapsed with laughter as he slipped it over his head. The tunic, which came only to Giacomello's knees, dragged below the ankles of the shorter Bernardone.

"This won't do. We'll have to get something from one of my brothers."

"No, no! I tell you it's perfect. The more foolish I look in people's eyes, the more they'll leave me free to focus on God."

"At least let me find you a belt to cinch it up out of the dust."

Francesco spotted a cord sticking out from beneath the bed.

"You see how God provides for His poor ones? Here is all the belt I need." He picked up the rope and looped it about his waist.

"Francesco! Have a little pity. Please," Giacomello pleaded. "All of Gubbio will soon know you're our guest. Think what they'll say about our family when they see how we've clothed you!"

The young man laughed again. "Tell them I'm crazy. Everyone in Assisi says so already. They can verify it with the next traveler from the south."

"He's hopeless," Giacomello shrugged to the disinterested tapestries insulating the cold stone walls. "Well, come now. Let's find out if you've gotten too ethereal to eat."

They left for the common hall. The old warrior, still not totally persuaded of his friend's conversion, immediately launched another foray. "Has the news reached Assisi that we're getting up an army again? We're going to put the Perugians in their place once and for all. You know, I could get you a captaincy with no trouble...."

# 8

# A Casa Spada

The whole Spada household—family, men-at-arms, craftsmen, and servants—were gathering in the great hall for the main refection of the day.

At one end of the long room an ornately-laid table stretched across a platform. This table was reserved for family members and special guests. It faced down the hall so those at the lesser tables could have an unobstructed view of their superiors. A huge silver saltcellar molded in the likeness of a battle-clad *destrier,* or war horse, was placed halfway down the trestle table nearest the family's. The most important retainers sat on the family side of this ornament while the rest of the commoners were ranged "below the salt."

At the end of the hall, opposite the high table, was the minstrel's gallery. The troupe struck up a lively melody as Giacomello entered with Francesco.

A small boy in page's livery approached them with a pitcher and basin. Francesco had dined with noblemen before, and was familiar with the ceremonial aspects of the meal. He washed his hands and dried them on the napkin draped across the boy's arm. The page then led him to his assigned place at the head table.

Federigo introduced Francesco to the *Nobildonna* Olivia, his mother, and to Villano, Bishop of Gubbio, who had come to pay his respects to the old woman and her sons.

The bishop had a reputation as a saintly man, and already the townspeople called him "Blessed" Villano. Certainly, he moved Francesco like no one he had ever met. The two men exchanged no words, yet a warm current of love and recognition passed instantly between them. Here, Francesco sensed, was another who understood, who knew what it meant to be consumed by Divine Fire.

"Bernardone has just arrived among us, Your Excellency," Federigo said. "He's looking for work. Preferably in the service of the church, I suspect. Am I too presumptuous, Francesco? I thought perhaps you could grant him an audience tomorrow."

"Tomorrow? Alas, no," the bishop replied. "Tomorrow I must separate an unhappy leper from his family and remove him to San Lazzaro. But come to me later this week if you wish."

Francesco bowed gratefully. *My Lord, how good You are to me,* he thought. *What pure joy it would be to serve You through this holy bishop.* He could scarcely believe how swiftly his fortunes were turning, that his trials of the past few weeks were to end so abruptly.

As Bishop Villano and Lady Olivia sat down at his right, he became aware suddenly that the meal was to be eaten in the courtly fashion, with each "knight and lady" pair sharing a single plate and goblet. Beyond them, Federigo and his wife were arranging themselves and at the center of the table Giacomello was talking to his teenage niece. She curtsied, turned, and glided toward Francesco. Again she curtsied, smiled politely, and waited for him to pull out the chair on his other side.

"You be very kind to Sior Bernardone, Amalia," her grandmother urged as the girl sat down. "He's had a very trying journey. Be sure he eats well."

Francesco grimaced at Spadalunga who was beaming at the young couple. Clearly he considered the arrangement a stroke of genius on his part. The lord of the household then seated himself to a flourish of trumpets and the parade of cooks and scullions began.

Antonio's daughter was a model young noblewoman—a courteous hostess, beautifully groomed, modest, cheerful and intelligent, doing her gracious best to put her nervous dining mate at ease. He might have been less nervous had he known she shared his low opinion of Giacomello's stratagem. To her, this was but another of Uncle's tricks to undermine her love for Giorgio di Marzialle. She disguised her annoyance flawlessly.

Soups, stews, and meat pies soon covered every area of the table. All of the game had been cut into small pieces, mashed into a soft mush, and spiced so highly that it was hard to tell one course from the next. Even the wine, breads, and cakes served with the hot courses were too spicy for Francesco's spartan stomach. He had not eaten like this in more than a year. Yet, the more he tried to refuse, the more seriously Amalia took her grandmother's orders.

"I heard the tocsin again today, Excellency," Lady Olivia said during a break between courses.

"Yes. Our ancient enemy the wolf again."

"Have you heard of our wolf, Sior Bernardone?" Amalia asked. "They say he is old as the mountains, clever as an owl, and strong as a great bear. No animal has ever spoiled our herds like this one."

"Animal?" Her grandmother sniffed. "That *thing* is no more an animal than the serpent in the Garden of Eden. It is *versipellis*, sent from hell!" She used the old Roman term for "werewolf."

"Well, Mother, man or beast, he has outdone himself in deviltry today," said Federigo. "The bells you heard were for the returning hunters. Your *versipellis* mauled one of the men so badly he bled to death before they could get him off the mountain."

Lady Olivia crossed herself. "Did they destroy the monster?"

"Still free. He got away from the men, but the dogs chased him further up into the hills."

"And the dogs?" asked Giacomello.

"I heard that two or three came in several hours after the hunters. As for the rest, no one knows."

The eldest brother banged his fist on the table. "Ha! They won't be back, take my word! He's done it again! God, if I had twenty fighting men with half the heart of that wolf, no one could stand against me." He stared directly at Francesco as he said this.

"Behold my son Giacomello, Your Excellency," Lady Olivia said. "He would enlist the legions of Lucifer if he thought they could defeat the Perugians."

"You're quite right, Mother," Spadalunga parried. "Unfortunately, the Perugians signed them up first."

At this everyone chuckled and turned expectantly toward the passageway leading from the kitchen. The chief cook himself, carrying his large wooden ladel (the insignia of his high office), was leading the procession. With ten courses already stuffed into their stomachs, and with Bishop Villano the honored guest, the diners were now looking forward to an especially festive dessert.

They were not disappointed. At Giacomello's nod, two scullions set a huge pie in front of the bishop.

"Would you please do the honors, Your Excellency?" said the chief cook with great dignity.

Bishop Villano knifed through the tender upper crust of the pie, then jumped back as three white doves stuggled through the slit and flew coo-ing to the rafters. The entire assembly applauded as the cook bowed and smaller pastries were distributed to the lower tables.

Finally it was time for the basins and towels again. The minstrels took their places as the pages and scullions cleared the last traces of the meal.

"For our Lord Spada. May his vigor never fail!" announced their leader, to more approving cheers. "A *chanson* of Bertrand de Born."

59

A second minstrel stepped forward and began singing in a slow, full-throated basso,

> My heart fills with gladness to see
> Strong castles besieged, and stockades smashed,
> Vassals cut down,
> While dead men's horses rove at will.
> When the battle is joined, let all men of good breed
> Think of naught but the breaking of bones,
> For 'tis better to die than be conquered alive.
> My greatest joy is hearing the shout
> "On! On!" from both sides
> And the neighing of riderless steeds,
> The groans of "Help me! Help me!"
> Or seeing the great and the small
> Lying in ditches and on the grass
> Transfixed by spear shafts!
> Lords, mortgage your domains, castles, and towns,
> But never forsake ye war!

Giacomello sighed when the music was done. "Bertrand de Born. Now *there* was a troubador!"

Francesco only pressed his palms against his groaning abdomen and wondered how long the Poverello could survive in this environment. He must seek out the bishop as soon as possible, no later than the day after next.

The following morning, after their light collation, Antonio took Francesco's arm.

"Come, I'll show you our factory," he said. "It's the building you saw outside the compound."

60

Spadalunga fired a dark look at his brother and strode abruptly from the hall.

"What was that about?" asked Francesco.

"Don't worry. It has nothing to do with us," Antonio said. "That was just our dear old Giacomello being true to his nature.

"Sad to say, his soul would be happier today had he fallen in battle twenty years ago. The age is changing, Francesco, and the changes have torn him apart. He still recalls a time when the common folk paid our keep, while we went to war to protect them. The clergy still tithes them to pray for their peasant souls, but they pretend they no longer need us to defend their bodies.

"On top of that, commoners are now being knighted! The bankers have forced us to sell our estates and move into Gubbio, even to support ourselves with our woolen mill. Other merchants are agitating to have our tax exemption taken away, regardless of our family name. They say it lets us compete with them unfairly. Even some of the nobility want all of our class who engage in business stripped of our rank and privileges. This would be the killing blow to Giacomello."

"And to you?"

Antonio shrugged. "The times are turbulent, but I am not a turbulent man. Federigo and I try to run our business quietly. We involve Giacomello as little as possible and leave him free to battle his phantoms."

Though they were new to commerce, the Spada brothers were clearly well-organized. The activity level in the mill was low that morning—because the bulk of the sheep shearing was still a month off—but already several people were busy at each work station.

At a high double-door, men were unloading a cart of fleeces, while

61

others sorted them on a table, separating the high-quality shoulder and side shearings from the tag ends. After the burrs and small twigs were picked out, the wool was scoured in large cauldrons, spread on sunlit arches to dry, then carded to separate and straighten the fibers for spinning. Several women were twirling cleaned and dried fibers on large drop spindles. Others were fabricating linens from the spun yarn, weaving them on hand looms that looked like small four-poster beds, or felting the fibers together to create bolts of flannel. At the final station, men with arms and faces and tunics pied by a rainbow of dyes dipped the linens or coarse yarn into various vats and hung their dripping artistry on drying racks.

"My father should be buying from you," Francesco said as they left the building. "Has he seen what you're making here?"

"No," Antonio said. "Selling has been a problem for us. We're planning to hire someone this spring to travel the district and..."

He paused. "I was thinking, Francesco, that if the bishop has nothing to your liking, you might work with us. You know all of the linen dealers in the area. And you'd have plenty of time to yourself on the road for your prayer and meditation."

"Thank you," Francesco said. "It's a kind offer. I need to pray very hard on all of this. So many choices have come up, but I don't know yet which is God's will for me."

"Of course."

It was almost midday. The cathedral bells began tolling slowly, each peal followed by a long funereal silence.

"The leper," Antonio said. "Have you ever witnessed the removal of a leper?"

Francesco's face contorted before he could control himself. "Never," he said. "In Assisi, I had to hold my kerchief to my nose if I came within half a league of the leprosarium. God forgive me, but I nearly vomited whenever I met one begging by the road, rotting before my eyes, moving like zombies. God knows what they've done to deserve their fate."

He trembled as he spoke, then flushed with shame. How great was the gulf still separating him from the Lamb sacrificed for *all* humankind.

"Come, Francesco," Antonio said gently. "Perhaps it is time to watch."

# 9

## Il Lebbroso

Within the half hour, Antonio, Francesco, and their bodyguard had arrived at the *Cattedrale* in the northern quarter of Gubbio. A small procession was moving up the steps of the cathedral, between the columns supported by kneeling marble oxen, and into the dim interior.

"Ah. It's Tafurino the candlemaker," Antonio said. "I expected as much."

The clatter and bustle in the street outside the cathedral subsided as the procession passed, out of respect for the cross flashing in the sunlight from its tall standard and for their bishop, who followed the cross-bearer. Behind Bishop Villano limped the leper himself.

The man fixed his eyes on the pavement, trying to ignore the bystanders. He knew what they were thinking. Their suspicions about him had at last been confirmed. They had been right to ostracize him when the whispering began the year before, when someone first noticed the redness and swelling of his face and the increasing hoarseness of his voice. They had stopped buying his candles. They kept their distance from him at church services, until finally he could stand it no longer and had isolated himself in his home.

His guildsmen, at least, had supported him while he came to grips with the inevitable. He knew they would also feed his family after his separation from the community. Even now they followed him into the cathedral in their gold-and-white livery, carrying the banner of their trade, a string of ten candles suspended above a vat of wax. "Light and Truth" was their motto; yet he must now enter the black mawl of Satan, the world of the living dead.

Francesco and Antonio followed as the leper was led past the statues and shadowy frescoes to the front of the cathedral. There, before the altar, a dark cloth was draped over two trestles. The candlemaker knelt beneath this pall and slurred his final confession. He kept his head bowed as the bishop began the requiem Mass for the dead and the gospel story of the ten lepers:

"As Jesus was entering the village, he was met by ten men with leprosy. They stood some way off and called out to him, 'Jesus, Master, take pity on us'…."

At the end of the service, Bishop Villano came down from the altar and spread the shroud over Tafurino. "Take this cloak," he said. "Put it on as a sign of humility and never leave without it. In the name of the Father, and of the Son, and of the Holy Spirit. Amen."

The leper was then led back through the church to the ambulatory where the bishop sprinkled him with holy water.

"Remember thine end and thou shalt never do amiss," he read. "Whence Augustine says, 'He readily esteems all things lightly, who ever bears in mind that he will die.'"

Tafurino raised his head for an instant when the bishop shoveled a spadeful of dirt from the cemetery over his feet. Francesco shivered involuntarily at the sight of the thick lips and bluish lumps and flattened nose showing where the cartilage had already begun to decompose.

"Be thou dead to the world," Bishop Villano continued, "but alive again unto God."

The line of marchers re-formed and moved again to the front steps of the cathedral. "Citizens of Gubbio," the bishop called out to the people in the square, "I commend this poor brother to your care."

The crowd swept back like a retreating tide as the cross, bishop, leper, and guildsmen passed through, then closed just as swiftly in their wake. The chanting of Bishop Villano and Tafurino's muted response— *Libera me, Domine... Libera me, Domine*—was soon overwhelmed by the rumbling of carts and the cries of vendors.

"Seen enough?" Antonio asked. "Or do you want to follow them to San Lazzaro?"

"To the end," said Francesco.

They caught up with the procession as it approached the Porta Santa Croce. The candlemaker was losing control as the full impact of leaving the city struck him, and his sobbing interrupted the repetition of the litany. Francesco noticed that Bishop Villano also passed his hand over his eyes several times as the leprosarium came into view.

The Spedale de San Lazzaro consisted of several squat white-washed buildings, providing separate housing for the men and women lepers and

67

the Benedictine monks and nuns who cared for them. The white walls formed a dazzling backdrop for the grey-robed specters emerging silently from their cubicles. The entire community had come out to see their new member. To Francesco, watching in horror from the top of the path, it seemed as though the tombs of the common graveyard were spewing up their skeletons one by one.

The city people stopped at a safe distance from the hospital. Bishop Villano stepped forward with Tafurino and was met by a young Benedictine carrying a cup, clapper, and gloves. The bishop addressed the leper one last time.

"My son, since childhood you have been instructed in the ten commandments of God. To these you must now add the following ten prohibitions:

"I forbid you ever to enter a church, a market, a mill, a bakehouse, or any assembly of able-bodied people;

"I forbid you to ever wash your hands or any of your belongings in any spring or stream of water of any kind, and if you are thirsty you must drink water from this cup or some other vessel;

"I forbid you ever henceforth to go out without your leper's garb, that you may be recognized by others, and you must not go outside your house unshod;

68

"I forbid you, wherever you may be, to touch anything you wish to buy other than with a rod or staff to show what you want;

"I forbid you ever henceforth to enter taverns or other houses if you wish to buy wine; and take care even that what they give you they put into your cup;

"I forbid you to be with any woman who is not of your family;

"I forbid you to touch infants or young people or to offer them any of your possessions;

"I forbid you, when you are on a journey, to answer anyone who questions you until you have gone downwind off the road; or to go through a narrow alley where those who meet you cannot avoid you;

"I forbid you, if you pass over some stile or rough ground, to touch any posts or things whereby you cross, until you have first put on these gloves;

"I forbid you henceforth to eat or drink in any company except that of lepers."

The bishop gave the cup and gloves to Tafurino. Then he handed him the wooden clapper, the ultimate symbol of his condition. "Take this *tentennella* and carry it with you always. You must sound it to warn others of your presence."

As he finished his admonitions, an older leper hobbled up and wrapped his stump of arm around the candlemaker. "Come, brother," he said huskily. "I'll show you to your cell."

"Don't touch me!" Tafurino cried as best he could. Then his whole body seemed to slump. He dropped his head and submitted to the man. Bishop Villano followed also and placed a coin in the bowl outside the new leper's room. The other lepers backed away so that the townspeople could follow the bishop's example.

Antonio took two coins from his purse and extended one to Francesco. "Would you give an alms?" he asked.

Francesco shook his head. "I can't, Antonio. But please, you give an extra amount for me."

For one last time, with a look of inexpressible sorrow, Tafurino raised his eyes and scanned his former townsmen. It seemed to Francesco that the leper stared especially long at him, perhaps because he was a stranger. Then he heard Bishop Villano saying, "Worship God and give Him thanks. Have patience and the Lord will be with thee."

The bishop raised his hand in benediction and the cortege, minus the one-time candlemaker, returned to Gubbio.

*"What is it you want of me, Francesco?"*

*"To know Your will, Lord. To know how You wish me to serve You."*

*"What work would you prefer?"*

*Francesco's mind flashed instantly to the bishop, but just as quickly he rejected the thought.*

*"You already know my mind, Lord. Grant that I may know Your will and have the strength to follow it."*

*"What work would you most abhor?"*

*So that was how it was going to be. Francesco's thoughts returned to his father's shop in Assisi. He saw himself again sorting through the bales of linen while Pietro cursed and fumed at his workers.*

*He would do it. He would even kneel and ask his father's forgiveness in the public square if God wanted him to.*

*He raised his head and looked into his Savior's eyes, prepared to see the worst. But what he saw there chilled him like a gust of wintry wind. It was the same look of infinite sadness, the very face of Tafurino the candlemaker, that had so appalled him earlier that day.*

*He was too unnerved even to reply.*

*"My beloved. All that you have ever loved carnally and vainly you must now reject for spiritual things. Take what seems bitter as sweetness and despise yourself if you would call yourself My follower."*

71

*Francesco grasped the hand extended to him and in the same instant found himself alone on a road flanked by a wide plain. The road disappeared around a hillock just ahead of him and as he stared in that direction he heard a faint knocking sound that grew gradually louder and nearer. Just as he realized what it was, the leper rounded the curve and came directly toward him.*

*The next few moments seemed like an eternity as the emaciated creature dragged nearer. Suddenly, an intense wave of compassion surged through Francesco and he rushed to the man. He took the leper in his arms and kissed his bloated lips. Then he knelt down and began kissing his hands and feet. But the wounds he kissed were not the usual lacerations of leprosy. They had been created by a sharp object driven through the flesh. Overwhelmed with emotion, he released his hold on the leper, and when he looked up, the man was gone.*

"Francesco! Francesco! Are you all right? You've been writhing on your mat like a demoniac."

He opened his eyes. Although it was still night, everything in the room, including Antonio bent over him, seemed to emanate a soft blue light.

"All right? Yes. I'm wonderful," he smiled.

Hunkering in the sunlight before his door the next morning, Tafurino the leper saw a young man descending the hill from the city. It was the friend of Antonio Spada who had witnessed his removal the day before.

"Peace and good to you, brother Tafurino," the stranger said. "Would you please point me to the prior's quarters?"

The leper did not answer immediately. Finally he murmured, "Last night I dreamed you kissed me. But ... I know I've never seen you before yesterday. Who are you?"

"My name is ... that is, I am called ... the Poverello. I've come to work."

# 10

# San Lazzaro

Father Matteo, the Benedictine priest assigned to teach the new orderly his duties, knocked gently at the door of the first leper. Francesco focused on the crucifix nailed to the outside of the door, bracing himself against the misery he was sure to find on the other side.

A nauseating stench wafted from the leper's cell as Matteo nudged the door open. Francesco swallowed hard against the pressure rising in his throat. He closed his eyes for an instant, recalling again his dream of the Christ-leper.

When he opened them again, he saw a murky figure hunched on a wooden chair in the corner. The man was tiny, even smaller than himself, and seemed ancient, though he was mostly hidden by his veil and grey sackcloth robe.

"Sunshine today, Tomas!" the monk called out in a loud voice. "Let's get you and this room some air."

He motioned Francesco to one side of the chair as he continued shouting to the leper. "This is our new brother, Poverello. He's going to take care of you. Hang on now." They lifted the old man, chair and all, and carried him outside.

Matteo wrapped a blanket around Tomas while Francesco replaced the sheet caked with dried blood and pus. Then the orderly sloshed water on the floor and began scrubbing.

"We'll be back in a few minutes to give you your bath," Matteo said. Tomas, starting to revive under the warm sun, nodded for the first time. The monk sent Francesco to the scullery for a bucket of hot water while he continued down the row of cells, rousting the more mobile lepers out of their rooms and into the daylight.

Francesco had never seen an advanced case of leprosy before. In fact, Tafurino was the first leper he'd looked at closely and his disease was still in its early stage.

Tomas was another story, however. Francesco, to his relief, did not retch with horror as he removed the veil from the old man's face. Instead, the visionless eyes, the red raw wound that had once been a nose, the festering lips, and the mushy flesh that passed for a chin quickly blurred as the pity welled within him. Then they uncovered Tomas' body, totally distorted with suppurating blue-black sores. Most of his fingers and toes were gone.

Father Matteo watched Francesco cautiously as he dipped towels in the hot water and placed them carefully on Tomas' skin. He drew out as much of the pus as he could, then patted him with a dry cloth and bandaged his hands and feet. Before he replaced Tomas' veil, Francesco kissed him as he had his dream leper.

76

"God's peace and good to you, Brother Tomas," he said.

The old man waved with his hand in reply.

"He wishes to thank you," Matteo said.

"He cannot speak, then?" Francesco asked.

The leper gestured toward his open mouth, and only then did Francesco notice the withered stump where his tongue should have been.

Matteo put his arm around Francesco's shoulder as they left Tomas' cell.

"The first bathing is always the hardest, brother. How do you feel?"

"I feel ashamed, Father. May God forgive me for the way I once despised His people."

"It's all right, Poverello. You understand now, and that's all that matters. You will do well with us."


After a few days at San Lazzaro, Francesco began exploring the hills and grottoes above the leprosarium during his work breaks. And soon, with the prior's permission, he had resumed his Assisan practice of praying in caves much of the night.

Prior Benedetto had been reluctant at first, mostly fearing for the Poverello's safety, but he also recognized that his new orderly had some special calling that went beyond his own understanding, beyond the young man's duties among the lepers.

In their first meeting, the newcomer had talked of his dream and the prior had shared readings from the scriptures and the rule of Saint Benedict that he felt would reinforce the man's insights. A passage from Isaiah, in particular, kept reemerging during Francesco's nightly vigils:

> He had no form or comeliness
>     that we should look at him,
> And no beauty that we should desire him.
> He was despised and rejected by men;
>     a man of sorrows and acquainted with grief;
> And as one from whom men hide their faces.
> He was despised and we esteemed him not…
> We esteemed him stricken,
>     smitten by God, and afflicted.
> But he was wounded for our transgressions…
> Upon him was the chastisement
>     that made us whole.

The lacerated lepers and his meditations on the crucified Messiah Whom they resembled took Francesco's understanding of poverty to a deeper level. He understood why the church labeled them *pauperes Christi*, Christ's paupers.

His own renunciation of Pietro Bernardone's wealth now seemed not so much an act of detachment as an act of anger and defiance against his father's attempts to dominate his life—an expression of his own immaturity rather than God's will. Surrendering his possessions was so insignificant compared to the physical poverty of his patients and their lives as social outcasts, virtual prisoners in the hospital. And beyond the lepers with their bodily suffering, Francesco began to glimpse a poverty of the *spirit* that his mind could barely grasp, the kind of mental anguish Jesus had felt in Gethsemane when He sweated blood, or when He had screamed from the cross, "Father! Why have You forsaken me?"

And so he prayed, night after night. "Lord, forgive my vanity in thinking I was ever one of Your poor. If You will it, scourge me as you have these lepers, make me hideous in the world's eyes, wound me with Your wounds. Let me share even Your emptiness of spirit, if You think I can bear it. Only grant me the grace to thank You and continue praising You if it should happen."

One night, as he prayed, his head became very heavy and slumped down against his chest. His body seemed paralyzed, as if he should be in a deep sleep, yet his mind remained calm and lucid. With his inner eye he watched as a wave of robed forms eddied through a crowd of villagers.

The robes were grey like his tunic and, also like his, were girdled by ropes. Those wearing the robes were hidden by their hoods, so he could not even see if they were men or women. They moved silently, anonymously, and (he sensed) almost protectively through a town that he did not know. They acted as a buffer, shielding another grey specter from the townspeople.

This central figure bent low on the back of a donkey, hunched like Tomas on his chair and apparently as helpless. Without seeing the face of the cowled figure, Francesco knew it to be that of a man almost totally blind and resigned to being led about like a child. His hands and feet were bandaged like a leper's and his body was sapped of all vitality.

"The wounds of Christ! The wounds of Christ!" boomed out a voice from the sea of grey. With each cry the excitement of the crowd increased and they pressed even harder, clamoring to reach the mounted figure. For his part, the man seemed completely insensible to the commotion.

Francesco shuddered as the ghostly procession swirled through the village and finally out of sight. His body relaxed and he stared blankly into the dark night enveloping the cave.

He was puzzled by the robed figures and the villagers but there was no doubting the meaning of the grey rider. "So be it, Lord. So be it," he prayed.

He was so absorbed he didn't even notice the twin pinpoints of orange eyeshine that returned his stare.

"You see, Poverello," Father Matteo was explaining, "these people have been thrust into our lazaretto entirely against their wills. They didn't ask God to become lepers, any more than you asked the Perugians to take you hostage."

Matteo laughed at Francesco's look of surprise. "Gubbio is too small and Sior Giacomello too loquacious for you to remain hidden for long. He and his brother Antonio came to visit you last evening. You were in the hills, so they had a long chat with us monks instead."

He shrugged. "Anyway, you are still the Poverello to me, if that's the way you want it. I only bring up the dungeon to help you understand.

"Lazars go through several phases, much as you must have seen among your fellow prisoners. At first they are shocked to find themselves here. No one ever imagines he or she will become leprous. That only happens to other, less worthy, people—the worst of sinners. Our new patient, Tafurino, is feeling such a shock still.

"Then they go through a period where they refuse to associate with the other lepers, still unwilling to accept their lot. They complain often to the monks or nuns, but are totally indifferent to the problems of their fellow sufferers.

"And finally, after some weeks, or months, or sometimes years, the change comes. They can no longer deny that they are part of a community, a community of exiles. Some react with rage, and become like animals, trying to terrorize and take advantage of the others.

"But a surprising number become deeply religious, turning their external pain into inner triumphs. It's wonderful, the way they love and care for one another. They're an inspiration to us who claim to be religious by profession."

"You are an inspiration, too, Father," Francesco said, "you and the others who serve the lepers. Only two weeks ago, I felt certain the straightest road to hell ran through a monastic courtyard."

"People are people, Poverello. Lazars and monks alike can be sacred or profane, just as soldiers can be brave or cruel, or merchants greedy or open-handed. Most of us spend our entire lives wavering between the extremes."

The Benedictine pointed to a small hut, somewhat removed from the other buildings. "Would you like to see one of our 'animals'?"

# 11

## Ubertino

"Ubertino Rosso has become so filthy we've had to isolate him from the others. For their sakes. He seldom comes out to use the common latrine, preferring to foul his own cell. If one of the brothers comes near the place, he shouts obscenities and blasphemes against God and His Holy Mother. It's all we can do to leave food outside his door without him throwing excrement at us. As you can imagine, neither he nor his cell has been cleaned in months."

"He sounds as though he might have a devil," Francesco said.

"Many of the brothers would swear it. They're terrified of the man. Certainly, if anger, and bitterness, and self-hatred are demons, he is thrice possessed."

Matteo stopped a short distance from the hut.

"Would you try to talk to him? You don't wear our habit. He may not turn on you as he has the rest of us."

The suggestion caught Francesco off guard. It also seemed a little preposterous. Who was he, that the leper should show him any special deference? Then he reminded himself that his will was no longer his own.

"Yes. Of course, Father," he replied. "I'll do what I can. With the help of God."

He lowered his head and prayed for that help as the Benedictine backed away toward the main complex.

Francesco had noticed the door of Ubertino's cell crack open slightly while he and the priest were talking. It closed quickly now as he approached. He sat down on the ground a few feet from the hut with his back to the only window. He could be watched without upsetting the watcher.

"Ubertino, I'd like to talk with you."

There was no answer, but Francesco could sense the leper's attention focused on his back.

"I only want to serve you, to ease your pain where I can. Tell your servant what to do."

A gravelly laugh crackled from within the building, a bitter, cynical laugh.

"Servant?" the leper rasped. "The priests' hireling wants to be my servant?"

84

Francesco did not respond. He sat calmly, gazing away from the cell. Ubertino had more to say.

"I had more servants than Job, once. Did you know that? The Rosso name is one of the oldest in the Tiber Valley. And now you come wanting to serve me. I would have dismissed you with an alms in the old days, boy, and been well rid of you.

"Did they tell you how I used to give alms, and freely too? I was a true patrician, providing for my own and the whole neighborhood as well. And look how I'm rewarded—cursed worse than Job on his dung heap ever was.

"I even have my own dung heap. Wouldn't you like to move closer so you can appreciate it more fully?"

"Job's curse was only a test of his trust in God," Francesco ventured. Rosso obviously felt some affinity with the patriarch, the original undeserving sufferer.

"But *he* was cured!" the man gurgled, straining to scream. "No one ever leaves this place. It's not a test, but a slow torment and torture unto death. That is how God thanks those who trust Him and try to do as He says!"

"Sior Rosso, if you have truly followed God's commandments in the past, He will not forsake you now. Tonight, I will pray that He grant you peace."

"Peace? Oh yes. Peace. It's easy for you to sit in the sunlight with your healthy limbs and talk of peace. But what peace would you have if you were all rotten and stinking?"

"Brother, the weaknesses of the body are given to us in this world for the eternal salvation of our souls. They can be of great merit if borne patiently."

At these words, the door flew open and Francesco was pelted by a malodorous shower. "Be patient? When my disease burns and crucifies me day and night? Get away from here and leave me alone! You're just like the priests!"

Instead of retreating from the barrage as the monks had, however, Francesco got up and walked to the open door. "You're right to vent your fury on me, Sior Rosso. I was once wealthy too and turned away from the lepers who needed my help. You punish me justly if not severely enough. Is there nothing more you would do to me?"

The leper had slumped down against the doorframe, exhausted emotionally and physically. "Just leave me alone," he said weakly.

"May I come back tomorrow? I would like to clean your room."

Ubertino Rosso nodded. "Would you wash me too? I smell so bad I can't stand myself."

Francesco raised him from his knees and held him in his arms for a moment. Then he helped the leper to his bed.

He left for his cave before the community supper, stopping only to get a half-loaf of bread and a cup for water from the cook.

His mind was troubled following his talk with Ubertino Rosso, and not only because of the man's despair. He remembered conversations from the past, when his father had spoken enviously of the Rosso family and their holdings. He wondered how Pietro Bernardone would feel if he could see the elder Rosso now, whether he would exult over a fallen rival, or might gain some insight into the futility of amassing and hoarding silver and land.

At a creek near the cave, Francesco stopped and disrobed. He rinsed his tunic in the clear water, and prayed that the leper's rage might be washed away as easily by God's clarifying grace, that his own heart might be purified of the lingering, sedimentary anger toward his father.

His mood lightened as the stream carried away the bits of excrete-
ment from his clothing and the sun beat warmly on his body. Naked as
he was, he felt a sudden oneness with the surrounding hillside, the tall
pines and cypresses that never aspired to be more than trees, the wild
grasses with their green, newly-forming heads—with the unhappy leper
at the base of the mountain who had been forcibly stripped of his
trappings, and even with Pietro who had once proudly and lovingly
cuddled his naked baby son.

Francesco spread his dripping tunic over a rock outside the cave. The
late afternoons and evenings were warm now and he felt no need to
kindle a fire. He sat before the mouth of the grotto, chewing absent-
mindedly at the bread, sipping creek water from his cup, until his body
seemed to meld into the landscape and he was once again a liberated
spirit.

Where he went in this state, how long he conversed, he could not
have said. But when he regained his senses, the night was far advanced.
The moon hung above the mountain like the lantern of some groping
angel feeling its way among the harsh grey rocks and dark woods, prying
out nature's most shadowy secrets.

Nor had he any idea how long the wolf had been watching him. He just opened his eyes and the animal was there, directly in front of him, about ten steps away. The wolf seemed very thin in the light of the moon-lantern, almost silvery-white, standing rigidly, his gaze fixed on the man before him, panting noiselessly.

# 12

# Fra Lupo

The first time the wolf had seen the man at the mouth of his cave, he had whirled and limped back into the trees as quickly as his injuries would allow. His side still ached where the hunter had clubbed him and his victory over the dog pack had been hard won. Each hound had sapped a bit more of his strength, had returned a few more of his slashing, biting, thrusts and he had barely overcome the last of the animals to challenge him.

He had moved back down into the hills outside Gubbio, but across the valley from the sheep pastures. He knew of a small stream there, where he could slake his thirst and soak away some of the pain pulsing through his muscles. He lay in a cave for several days, too weak to hunt, too tired to move beyond the nearby creek. At his age, the healing came slowly and he had felt a strong urge to crawl into the darkest corner of the cave and lie down one last time.

But in the end he had emerged from his catacomb, his hip joints yielding stiffly to his craving for food. Running down live game was out of the question and he did not dare come any closer to the city. He found a nest of quail eggs, mostly because he could not follow when the mother feigned a broken wing and tried to lead him away. A few days later he found a dead squirrel on the ground and for the first time violated his rule against eating food he had not killed himself. He was near starvation and had to risk the possibility that the animal had been poisoned.

It was after he had finished the squirrel that he returned to his cave and found the man kneeling at the entrance. The wolf had hobbled away, but stopped when he realized the human was not giving chase. During the several hours he had watched from his brush cover, the man hardly moved, not until the sun drove the darkness from the forest. Then he stood up and walked dreamily down the hillside toward the city.

The man became a regular nighttime visitor to the cave, and the wolf, once he realized he was in no danger, found himself watching more from curiosity than caution. The kneeling figure seldom changed position, but sometimes he made a low crooning noise, "My God and my all, my God and my all," over and over again, so softly that it reminded the wolf of the regular breathing of his mate, in the winter days when she had curled for warmth against his side. The man was, in fact, so obviously harmless, so comfortable in the cave, that the wolf hardly regarded him as an intruder after the first few nights.

As his hunger grew and his stomach shrunk tighter and tighter up against his spine, there had been moments when he had seen the visitor as a possible prey. Certainly, slipping in behind him and snapping his neck would have been as easy as killing a helpless cub. And perhaps that had something to do with his hesitation. Like his mate, like their cubs, the man somehow offered the wolf a peaceful link to another creature and eased his loneliness ever so slightly. He began to welcome the regularity of the visits.

Perhaps the man felt a similar emptiness. Sometimes the wolf saw his whole body tremble while he made whimpering noises like a wounded animal. On such occasions the beast could sense the human's agitation.

But at other times, the man would flash his teeth, though his eyes stayed closed, and his voice would rise like a joyful howl. The wolf was tempted to howl with him, but chose to remain the silent observer.

Late one afternoon, he watched the man climb the hill, remove his covering, and wash it in the stream. Only after the visitor had settled like a scrawny, hairless bear before the cave did the wolf leave for his evening hunt. He was moving with a bit more freedom now, and was able to catch a tiny field mouse. Nearby he sniffed out its nest of blind, pink newborn— hardly a meal, but enough to fend off starvation for another day. He returned to the cave to check on his man, not even bothering to conceal himself anymore. He had stopped a few strides in front of the cave entrance when the human opened his eyes and spoke to him.

"Brother Wolf. I'm glad you've come. I want to talk to you."

The noises coming from the man's throat meant nothing to the wolf, but their tone was mild and he held his ground. He crouched to spring and growled a warning, however, when the man extended his hand toward him.

"Don't be afraid. Would you like some food? I only have this bread, but you're welcome to it." The man pulled apart the object in his hand and tossed a piece to the animal. The wolf smelled it suspiciously. The scent was unfamiliar.

"It's safe. Look." The man took a bite from the bread still in his hand. The wolf snapped up the piece from the ground. It was very dry and tasteless to the carnivore, but at least it was *food*.

The hand holding the rest of the bread was extended toward him again. He barked another warning, but the man did not flinch. Carefully the animal drew to within a single step, then snatched the bread from the hand and leaped away. The man did not move other than to replace his hand in his lap.

"You needn't fear me, Brother Wolf. I know you've done great harm in this region and everyone is right to cry out against you. The whole city sees you as its enemy, and wants to put you to death like any other robber or murderer. I don't share their feelings, though."

For the first time, almost in spite of himself, the wolf wagged his tail. Though he couldn't comprehend the words, he did understand that this was a friend and he moved closer when the man patted the ground beside him.

"Come sit with me, brother. I want to make peace between you and the citizens, so you won't harm them anymore, and they won't set their hunters and dogs on you."

Through the night the man talked. The wolf listened, allowed himself to be touched and petted. He winced once, just at daybreak, when the man accidentally stroked the blood-encrusted wound in his side.

"Ah. You've been badly hurt. I didn't know. You're much older than I expected, too. You shouldn't be up here alone in your condition, my brother.

"You must come with me to the city. I'll ask the villagers to give you the food and care you need. They will understand that you only acted from hunger in the past and protect you from hunger in the future. Come. Come with me now."

The man rose and put on his covering and beckoned to the wolf to follow. The animal limped beside him as he started down the path toward Gubbio.

"I know the perfect home for you, where lives another old warrior who would honor you as a comrade-in-arms. I've heard him praise your valor already. You might even become a good influence on him. When he sees that you have retired from your fierce ways in your old age, he may be more willing to accept peace himself."

At the bottom of the hillside, the trees gave way to a broad plain extending several hundred meters to the city walls. Here the wolf hesitated. The man knelt down and put his arm around the animal's neck.

"Come, brother. Just a bit more. You will be protected by the respect the people bear Sior Spada and his family. I myself will talk to the citizens on your behalf."

The wolf followed reluctantly and his tail began to droop.

"Not like that, brother, or you will have every dog in Gubbio besetting you. Carry yourself nobly. And while we walk, I'll tell you a tale I heard from a traveler some years ago.

"It concerns a great king who liked nothing more than a boisterous cock fight. He had purchased an especially strong young cockerel and kept asking the trainer when it would be ready for battle.

95

"'Not yet, Your Majesty,' said the trainer. 'He is too full of fire and picks quarrels with all the other birds. He is conceited and too proud of his strength.'

"When the king returned after two weeks, the trainer said, 'Still not ready. He becomes too excited when he hears another cock crow.'

"Another week passed, but again the trainer insisted the cockerel was not ready. 'No, Your Majesty. His feathers still bristle and he looks angry when he sees the other males.'

"Finally, the trainer gave his approval. 'The bird is marvelous,' he said. 'When another cock crows, he doesn't even blink. He is as calm and immobile as a carved bird. The others will take one look at him and fly in terror.'

"And so should you be, Brother Wolf. You must enter the city like a true soldier, head high. Pay the yapping dogs of Gubbio no attention. They will feel your strength and scurry back into their alleys."

Their entry might have been considered somewhat less than triumphal, however, given their motley appearance—the orderly in his oversized grey tunic, much dirtier than the day he received it from Giacomello Spada; the limping wolf with his grey fur caked and matted with mud and burrs. No one saw them but the gatekeeper, who only let them pass when Francesco insisted he was delivering the animal to Sior Spada who would be responsible for its behavior.

96

"It's him!" was all he could say.

Francesco nodded and smiled. Then he motioned the crowd to silence again.

"I'm entrusting Brother Wolf to the special care of Sior Giacomello Spada. They have both survived many battles in their lifetimes and will have many a rousing tale to trade in front of the fireplace."

The citizens cheered as Francesco turned to his friend.

"What do you say, Giacomello. Do you have room in your home for an aged warrior?"

Giacomello dropped to one knee so that he was eye-to-eye with the wolf. "I would be honored," he said. "And you must come with us, Francesco, and tell me how this happened."

Francesco stood up and the crowd cleared a path for the three comrades. "I can go with you as far as your gate," he said, "but I can't stay beyond that. God's needy come in human form too, and one of them is waiting for me now back at San Lazzaro."

They marched directly to the Piazza del Mercato, where the man seated himself on the edge of the fountain, the wolf at his feet, and waited. A boy carrying a yoke of buckets to the fountain was the first to see them. Francesco sent him running to the Spada compound to fetch Giacomello, which the youngster was only too happy to do. He knew something important was about to happen and was excited to be a part of it.

Two stray dogs sniffing around the edges of the square spotted the wolf and started barking, but as Francesco had predicted, they kept their distance. Shutters opened one by one, and suddenly the square seemed to leap to life. People tumbled out of their houses, fumbling at their clothes, shouting to one another.

"The wolf! The wolf! Someone has captured the wolf!"

"Single-handed! It's the friend of the Spada brothers!"

"Come see for yourself! He's holding him in the marketplace!"

Francesco sat quietly, scratching the wolf's head, until the piazza was nearly full. Then he raised his arms for silence. Once again, as in his Tripudianti days, he was the performer, the leader of the festivities, and the crowd responded to his direction.

"Dear people of Gubbio," he began when the buzzing had subsided, "Brother Wolf, whom you see standing here peacefully before you, has agreed to harm no man or beast ever again if you will feed him and keep him from hunger. And I pledge myself as his bondsman, that he will keep his end of the agreement. What do you say? Will you respect him and accept him as a friend into your community?"

The crowd was so amazed by the novelty of the scene that the "ayes" came slowly at first, but then the crescendo rose until the whole gathering was chanting sportively "aye, aye, aye," when Giacomello forced his way to the front of the circle. His mouth gaped open when he saw Francesco and the animal.

# 13

## Il Purgato

Going down from Gubbio, Francesco pondered his meeting with the wolf. Their closeness during the night and early morning had seemed so natural that he had no sense of anything unusual happening.

Yet, passing through the crowd with the animal and Giacomello Spada, he had heard several of the townspeople murmuring about a "miracle." Even Giacomello, when they parted at the gate of the Spada compound, seemed to regard him strangely, or at least differently. There was none of the usual bravado in his voice when he vowed to treat the wolf like a member of his own household. And when he asked Francesco to rejoin them soon, he added that he understood his friend's need to work among the lepers—a complete reversal for the old soldier.

Well, perhaps a miracle *had* happened, at least within the usual scope of human expectations. And maybe that's all a miracle really was—something outside the province of man's day-to-day experience. At those rare moments when we break through to the *supernatural*, Francesco reasoned, we feel we've touched the miraculous. Yet is this not the accustomed world of spirits, of God and his angels, of the arch-enemy and his forces, of the souls of the dead?

He supposed he should feel surprised about the wolf, yet he did not. Perhaps he was finally making some spiritual progress, in that he could now accept the touch of divine intervention as no more extraordinary than a father's caress.

He turned his thoughts to Ubertino Rosso, who could *not* see the paternal hand in his suffering. He prayed that both the aged signore's mental anguish and his physical suffering might be diminished.

"I know all things are possible to You, Lord, and that You wish Your children to be whole and healthy. Pardon my presumption, but perhaps You have tested Sior Rosso too harshly. Instead of bringing him closer to You, his trials have only turned him against You. If You bend him further, I fear he will break. Be gentle with him, Lord, and return him to Your love."

The whitewashed buildings of the leprosarium were below him now, shining brilliantly in the late-morning sun. He realized suddenly that Ubertino had been expecting him for over an hour and quickened his pace toward the scullery. His mind was on details now—hot water; a pitchfork and shovel, wash cloths, a brush and broom; clean bed linen and a cart to haul away the mess from the old man's cell.

Ubertino did not seem annoyed at his late arrival, however. When Francesco arrived with his paraphernalia, the leper was waiting calmly on his bed, in much the same state as the orderly had left him the previous afternoon.

Francesco carried the old man's chair outdoors. "You may want to wait in the sunshine while I clean your room," he suggested. Ubertino followed slowly, but sat on the grass instead.

"The chair needs washing too," was his only comment.

"I was in Gubbio this morning," Francesco said cheerfully as he began his task of shoveling, scraping, and scrubbing the leper's cell. "The wolf was brought into town, as peaceful as a cooing turtledove. He provided a great lesson for us all, showing how God can tame even the most savage natures, the angry beast in each of us."

Ubertino said nothing, but turned his body so he could watch the orderly work. He neither apologized for the condition of his cell nor offered to help. He reminded Francesco of an elderly gentlewoman he had seen once, staring sadly at a puddle flowing from beneath her skirts where she had urinated involuntarily. Francesco also recalled that she, like Rosso, retained a kind of dignity that placed her above embarrassment for her action.

By noon, the room had been restored to habitable condition. Francesco stepped outside just as the great bell of the cathedral began tolling the *Angelus.* He prayed the formula aloud and rejoiced to hear Ubertino's creaky voice join in the responses.

"The angel of the Lord appeared to Mary."

"And she conceived of the Holy Spirit..."

"Behold the handmaiden of the Lord."

"Be it done to me according to your word..."

The last reverberations from the bell slipped through the mountain passes and Francesco turned to his patient.

"I'm going to the refectory now. Would you like to eat with the community today?"

"You haven't bathed me yet," Ubertino replied.

"I understand. I'll bring your food when I return."

A few moments later, Francesco was back with two bowls of soup. He handed one to the leper and sat down on the grass beside him. Ubertino, unable to manipulate the spoon properly, held the bowl in his two hands, supping up the broth. He did not resist when the orderly offered to feed him the solid pieces, yielding like a small, hungry child to each approaching spoonful.

When they had eaten, Francesco left again, this time returning with a bucket of hot water and a wash basin.

"Look, Sior Rosso," he called out. "Brother cook has added his sweetest-scented herbs to your bath water. Everyone is elated by your change of spirit."

Again Ubertino did not comment, but it seemed to Francesco that he managed a slight smile, hopefully heartfelt. They went inside for the bath and the young man could sense the signore's approval of his housecleaning. The walls were still stained a dingy yellow and would have to be

102

whitewashed again. The odor would be lingering for several days yet. But every trace of filth was gone and smooth clean sheets graced the mattress.

"The building will need a good airing for several days yet. But once you're bathed and dressed in fresh clothing, you could move back with the other men. I hope you will want to do so."

Ubertino sat with his tunic swaddled around his thighs as the orderly knelt and began washing his feet. He sighed contentedly as he felt the warm water draw the itching and burning from his festering sores. He was puzzled, however, when he saw tears in the younger man's eyes.

"Sior Rosso, do you know the psalm *Jubilate Deo?*"

"I haven't prayed in years. Why do you ask me such a thing?"

"Look at your feet; then let us sing God's praises together."

The leper's feet, which moments before had been lump-encrusted alabaster stumps, had become as perfectly-formed and normally-pigmented as those of a healthy man. Even the toes he had lost years before had been restored.

His voice was even huskier as he urged, "My legs! Please! Wash my legs!"

Francesco's song rose emotionally as he resumed bathing his patient. After a few repetitions, Ubertino joined in the psalm, singing louder and stronger as each part of his body was purged of disease.

Jubilate Deo omnis terra;
psalmum dicite nomini ejus;
date gloriam laudi ejus...
Venite, et videte opera Dei!

Rejoice to God, all the earth;
sing in honor of His name; give Him glorious praise...
Come and see the works of God!


Francesco and Ubertino stood at a respectful distance from Bishop Villano's throne while the prelate and Prior Benedetto conferred sub rosa. The bishop nodded occasionally in response to the monk's excited whispering. Finally, Paolo, the bishop's messenger, returned with the city physician and the entire group gathered before the dais.

Ubertino disrobed and endured with great stateliness the prodding and probing of the doctor.

"There's no rational explanation, Excellency," the latter said at last. "It's hard to believe this gentleman was ever poxed in any way. There's not the slightest trace of a scar or blemish anywhere on his body."

"Thank you," said the bishop. "Paolo, conduct our physician to the scribe's chambers and have a bill of health drawn up for Sior Rosso."

Bishop Villano smiled fondly at Francesco while Ubertino put his tunic on again. Then he addressed the leper.

"My dear signore, you have been enormously favored by God today. He has restored you to the world of the living, overlooking your many blasphemies against Him. For while He is a just judge, His nature is ever to forgive and look with mercy upon His children. Clearly He wishes you to spend your last years in peace, among family and friends, in prayer and thanksgiving, preparing your soul for its coming encounter with Him.

"You may remain here with us until we find you a suitable escort south to your own district. Do you wish to return to San Lazzaro now with Prior Benedetto and Sior Bernardone to retrieve your possessions?"

"No, Your Excellency. One does not enter again voluntarily into the fires of hell."

"Praise God that your hell was but a purgatory. Now, please wait for me in the anteroom while I speak with these caretakers of yours."

Ubertino bowed and started to leave. Then he spun around to Francesco and burst into tears as he knelt before the young man. "How can I ever thank you?" he cried.

Francesco was embarrassed and dropped to his knees in turn. "Please. You mustn't do this, Sior Rosso. I was but your co-witness. The act was God's."

The bishop chuckled jovially. "Prior Benedetto, would you help both of these humble gentlemen to their feet? And be content to know, the two of you, that you each played a role to the greater glorification of God."

"This one, he is a *saint,* Your Excellency!" Ubertino wailed, then left the hall, sobbing. Francesco swallowed at the lump in his own throat and regained his composure while Bishop Villano ruminated.

"Well, my son," he began in the most soothing of tones, "you must be aware that you've really done it now."

"Your Excellency?"

"I had just learned of your conversion of the wolf when you arrived with Sior Rosso. The whole town has apparently been talking about you this morning, and when the good physician spreads his news they'll likely go insane.

"You heard what Sior Rosso said just now. Do you have any sense of the burden placed on you when the populace regards you as a living saint?"

Francesco hung his head. "I've heard Your Excellency's name mentioned in such terms."

"Exactly so. I know whereof I speak. And I thank God daily that I am protected by my office. They see my bishop's robes and maintain a respectful distance. But you, I fear, they might shred for relics.

"Oh, don't look so startled. I'm exaggerating, though how much or how little I honestly can't say. I daresay, they might actually strip you naked trying to get pieces of your clothing."

As if in confirmation of the prelate's words, Paolo reentered and announced that a crowd was gathering before the palace, including many on crutches and litters. Through the open door they could hear the uproar building: "Poverello! Poverello! Poverello!"

Bishop Villano scowled. "You must hurry back to the leprosarium where you will be safe from the townspeople. You can escape through one of the alleys behind the palace. Come, let me bless you quickly."

Francesco genuflected and kissed the bishop's ring.

"My son, I believe that God has some important use for you. I also feel that He plans to use you up entirely, until there's nothing left of your former self. I pray that you will always be able to hear His intentions for

you, and that He will provide you with the grace and strength to carry out those intentions. Go now in peace and love, in the name of the Father, and of the Son, and of the Holy Spirit."

"Amen," Francesco responded as he crossed himself.

"Prior Benedetto, I place our young friend in your protection. Guard and guide him as you would your own dear child."

"Yes, Excellency."

"Now go. Paolo will show you out. And God speed you both."

# 14

# Bernardo

The tension gripping Francesco gradually eased as he and Prior Benedetto approached San Lazzaro. The familiar buildings felt like home to him now, a welcome refuge from the delirium raging in the city.

Notoriety was the last thing he had expected. All he had ever really wanted to do was worship God in peace and anonymity. The leprosarium had seemed like the perfect haven for escaping from the world.

Apparently, God viewed his stay at San Lazzaro differently. He had used the leper Ubertino to drag Francesco into the very center of a great commotion, the one place he did not want to be.

He recalled what a mariner had once told him about the calm eye in the midst of the hurricane. "Lord," he prayed silently, "if You must embroil me in a storm, at least grant me the grace to stay focused in Your peace, to observe the storm from Your calm center and not be swept off by it."

The late afternoon sun had ducked half-hidden behind the western range. The white structures of San Lazzaro seemed to catch fire for a moment, glowing orange and pink on their southwestern walls, a deep magenta on their shaded sides. As if to punctuate the impression, the lepers emerged one by one from their cells, looking for all the world like crumbling burned-out coals in their black tatters, heaped in shapeless lumps before their darkened doorways. Francesco could hear them calling across to one another, their crackly voices sputtering and hissing like hot gases.

"He's coming!"

"The Poverello's back."

Their cries became more insistent as he and the prior passed between the rows of cells.

"Poverello, cure me!"

"Cure me too!"

"You must bathe us also," yelled one of the women. "It's not fair that you wash only the men!"

Those who were able began to press toward him, slowly and tortu- ously like a macabre army of ghouls. The few monks and nuns who happened to be nearby tried to herd them off while Francesco raised his arms desperately.

"No, my brothers and sisters. It's not I. Not I, but God. Please understand. *Not I, but God!*"

"Go back to your cells, all of you," Prior Benedetto commanded. "Can't you see he's already exhausted by the day's happenings? Get back!"

Prior Benedetto pushed Francesco toward his office. A woman threw herself into his path, trying to kiss his feet. The orderly stumbled and fell to one knee. Again the lepers lurched toward him, but the prior lifted him quickly by the arm and the two hurried into the main building.

"They've never been like this before," Prior Benedetto said when he had regained his breath. "It frightens me."

He paced the length of his office several times and mopped his forehead with the sleeve of his robe. "I think it would be best if you left us, my young friend. We have to be able to maintain order here. I doubt if that will be possible with you around."

"Just let us touch him," one of the lepers pleaded. "Just the hem of his tunic."

Another cried out more angrily. "He *must* cure me! He healed Rosso who did nothing but curse God day and night. I spend all my time praying. It's only right I should be healed too!"

"Brother, Sior Rosso lacked your strength," Francesco said. "Thank God that you're still able to pray in your affliction. Don't be envious of God's generosity, but be glad for your brother's joy."

"Damn Rosso and his joy," the patient protested, "and damn you too if you don't heal us!"

"But perhaps they *can* be cured, Father."

"And what if they can't? You saw how worked up they are. Imagine their disappointment if you should fail. There's no predicting how they might react.

"No. Bishop Villano entrusted your safety to me, and I'm afraid you might come to harm if you remain with us. Is there no other place you could go, at least for the present?"

Francesco was perplexed by the abrupt turn of events. "San Damiano, outside Assisi. The priest there has been my one friend this past year. I could return to him and work at restoring his church."

"Yes. That sounds like a good choice. Probably the sooner you leave, the better." The prior tugged reflectively at his earlobe. "Would you mind spending the night in your cave as you've been doing? I'll have the cook pack you a supper and food for your journey. I don't think it would be wise for you to be here in the morning."

"As you wish, Father."

Sad and bewildered, Francesco slipped through the city gates at the first light of morning. He kept his face hidden deep beneath his cowl and went directly to the Spadas' woolen mill. There he waited in a shadowed corner for Antonio to arrive. His gaze drifted to a solitary olive tree espaliered against a wall opposite the factory. Its flowers of early spring had dropped away and the first clusters of small green fruit swelled in their place.

For over an hour he huddled unnoticed. The men and women who worked in the mill straggled up in groups of two or three and were let in by the foreman. Finally, Antonio and Federigo rounded a corner of the shop in the company of an elegantly dressed nobleman. They were followed by a train of horses, servants, and bodyguards.

Francesco watched as they led the gentleman to the loading area. Workers began tying bundles of fabric onto the horses while the two brothers walked off to check other details. Seeing his chance, Francesco scurried after and caught up to them just before they entered the building.

"Antonio. Federigo. A moment, please."

"Francesco! What's the matter?" said Antonio. "You look scared out of your wits!"

"So I am," he replied. "It would take too long to explain, and I'm not really sure I could. Anyway, that's not why I've come. I have to return to Assisi and I couldn't leave without saying goodbye."

Federigo was eyeing him curiously. "Francesco, people have been calling you 'the blessed Poverello' and 'San Francesco.' I swear by all that's holy, they're even calling Giacomello's wolf 'San Lupo.'"

"I think you begin to understand my problem, then. The lepers are in a frenzy too."

"But…is it true? I mean…are you a saint, Francesco?"

114

"Federigo, don't even put such thoughts into my head. God knows what I am and what I've been. For myself, I'm not that certain anymore. I'm mostly feeling…confused. I need to go where I can be alone for a while and find some answers."

"All of Gubbio will be dismayed," Antonio said, "and you know that we will miss you sorely. Your departure couldn't be better timed, though."

"How so?"

"One of your fellow Assisans has just purchased a large quantity of cloth from us. He'll be leaving shortly with a well-armed company. You may be acquainted with him already—Lord Bernardo, the son of Quinta-valle di Bernardello."

"Only by reputation. He is a noted biblical scholar in our commune. His family is also one of the wealthiest in Assisi, but I don't suppose that's his fault." Francesco managed a smile for the first time that morning.

"Well, I find him a brilliant and charming man," Antonio said. "We talked most of the day yesterday. He has degrees in both civil and canon law, but his interest seems focused on spiritual matters. I hope you won't be offended, but your name did come up in our conversation. He expressed disappointment at not being able to meet you in person. I think you'd find each other welcome and well-suited companions on your journey. What do you say?"

Before Francesco could state his misgivings, their group was joined by Bernardo himself, a tall refined middle-aged man with an ethereal air of serenity that immediately put the younger man at ease.

"Pardon my intrusion, Sior Spada," he apologized, "but my troupe and I are ready to take our leave now."

Antonio glanced at Francesco, who nodded his agreement.

"Have you room for one more fellow traveler? This is Sior Bernardone, the friend we spoke of yesterday. As chance would have it, he's also returning to Assisi this morning."

Bernardo seemed mildly surprised as he studied Francesco. "I've heard stories of the changes in you since the days you worked for your father. At last I see the truth of the tales myself. Your company during our journey would do us honor, Sior Bernardone. I would be even more honored personally if you would stay on as my guest once we've returned to Assisi. My mind has been troubled lately and there is much I wish to ask you."

Francesco was too taken by the man's sincerity and good will to feel discomfited by his obvious admiration. He felt his heart opening to this nobleman lawyer and agreed without another thought.

The Assisan party drew up next to them, waiting for their master's signal. "God speed you both," the Spada brothers called out as Francesco and Bernardo climbed up onto their horses and moved to the head of the line of riders.

As his mount approached the lone olive, its heavily-pruned cruci-form limbs stretched tautly along their training wires, Francesco turned and waved a last farewell to his friends.

On to Assisi and whatever lay ahead!

# Epilogue

Francis returned to San Damiano, the first of three churches outside Assisi that he repaired with his own hands. Gradually, he was joined in his work by other men who saw in his lifestyle a most perfect path to God. The first to arrive was the nobleman Bernard of Quintavalle who, in obedience to the scriptures, gave all his wealth and possessions to the poor before coming to Francis.

From these seeds grew the organizations known today as the three orders of St. Francis. Most people who know of Francis are familiar with these groups. Yet what is not often recalled is that their universally-beloved founder was once but a post-adolescent on the road with no food, money, clothing, job, family, friends—nothing to sustain him but his trust in and love for God.

# For Further Reading

The following books are recommended if you want to learn more about the life and times of St. Francis. The primary sources concentrate on Francis himself; the secondary sources provide background information about his world.

## Primary Sources

Bonaventure, Saint, *The Life of St. Francis*, Paulist Press, NY, 1978.

Chesterton, G.K., *St. Francis of Assisi*, Geo. H. Doran, NY, 1924.

Cunningham, Lawrence, *Saint Francis of Assisi*, Harper & Row, NY, 1981.

Fortini, Arnoldo, *Francis of Assisi* (Helen Moak, translator), Crossroad, NY, 1981.

*Francis and Clare: The Complete Works* (Regis J. Armstrong, translator), Paulist Press, Ramsey, NJ, 1982.

Kazantzakis, Nikos, *St. Francis*, Simon & Schuster, NY, 1962.

*St. Francis of Assisi: Omnibus of Sources* (Marion A. Habig, editor), Franciscan Herald Press, Chicago, 1983.

*The Little Flowers of St. Francis* (Raphael Brown, translator), Doubleday (Image Books), Garden City NY, 1958.

Thomas of Celano, *St. Francis of Assisi*, Franciscan Herald Press, Chicago, 1963.

Timmermans, Felix, *The Perfect Joy of St. Francis*, Doubleday (Image Books), Garden City NY, 1955.

## Secondary Sources

Armstrong, Edward A., *St. Francis: Nature Mystic*, Univ. of California, Berkeley, 1973.

Goad, Harold Elsdale, *Franciscan Italy*, Methuan & Co., Ltd., 1926.

Heer, Friedrich, *The Medieval World*, World Publishing, 1961.

Martines, Lauro, *Power and Imagination: City-States in Renaissance Italy*, Alfred Knopf, 1979.

McCracken, Laura, *Gubbio, Past and Present*, David Nutt, 1905.

*The Music of the Troubadours* (Peter Whigham, editor), Ross-Erikson, 1979.

Richards, Peter, *The Medieval Leper*, D.S. Brewer, Ltd., 1977.

Rubin, Stanley, *Medieval English Medicine*, David & Charles, Newton Abbot, Devon, 1974.

Tuchman, Barbara, *A Distant Mirror*, Ballantine, NY, 1978.

Underhill, Evelyn, *Mysticism*, E.P. Dutton, NY, 1961.